Kids Learn!

Getting Ready for

5th Grade

Contributing Author

Chandra Prough, M.S.Ed.
National Board Certified Teacher

Publishing Credits

Conni Medina, M.A.Ed., *Managing Editor*; Robin Erickson, *Production Director*; Lee Aucoin, *Creative Director*; Timothy J. Bradley, *Illustration Manager*; Aubrie Nielsen, M.S.Ed., *Senior Editor*; Caroline Gasca, M.S.Ed., *Editor*; Melina Sánchez, *Assistant Editor*; Marissa Rodriguez, *Designer*; Stephanie Reid, *Photo Editor*; Rachelle Cracchiolo, M.S.Ed., *Publisher*

Image Credits

All images Shutterstock.

Teacher Created Materials

5301 Oceanus Drive
Huntington Beach, CA 92649-1030
http://www.tcmpub.com
ISBN 978-1-4333-2537-3
© 2014 Teacher Created Materials, Inc.

Table of Contents

Introduction

Weekly Activities for Students

Preparing Your Child for Assessments

Appendices

Índice de materias

Introducción

Actividades semanales para estudiantes

Preparar a su hijo para las evaluaciones

Apéndices

Welcome to Kids Learn!

Dear Family,

Welcome to *Kids Learn! Getting Ready for 5th Grade*. Fifth grade will be an exciting year, with plenty of new educational opportunities. For example, your child will learn about text structure, long division, and the coordinate plane! Interesting new topics in science and social studies will keep students engaged in lessons at school as well.

Kids Learn! was designed to help solidify the concepts your child learned in fourth grade and help your child prepare for the year ahead. The activities are based on the Common Core State Standards and provide practice with essential skills for the grade level. Keeping the skills your child learned in fourth grade sharp while on break from school will help his or her fifth grade year get off to a great start. There is also a section at the end of the book that provides practice for standardized testing.

Keep these tips in mind as you work with your child through the *Kids Learn!* book:

- Set aside a **specific time each day** to work on the activities.

- **Complete one language arts and one mathematics page** each time your child works in the book rather than an entire week's worth of activity pages at one time.

- Keep all **practice sessions with your child positive and constructive.** If the mood becomes tense or if either of you gets frustrated, set the book aside and find another time for your child to practice.

- **Help your child with instructions,** if necessary. If your child is having difficulty understanding what to do, work through some of the problems together.

- Encourage your child to do his or her best work and **compliment the effort that goes into learning.** Celebrate the completion of all the activities by filling in the certificate at the end of the book and displaying it in a special place.

Enjoy the time learning with your child during his or her vacation from school. Fifth grade will be here before you know it!

Bienvenidos a Kids Learn!

Querida familia:

Bienvenidos a *Kids Learn! Getting ready for 5th Grade*. El quinto grado será un año emocionante con bastantes nuevas oportunidades para aprender. Por ejemplo, su hijo aprenderá sobre la estructura de los textos, la división larga y los planos de coordenadas. Nuevos temas interesantes en las ciencias y estudios sociales mantendrán a los estudiantes interesados en las lecciones escolares.

Kids Learn! fue diseñado para ayudar a consolidar los conceptos que su hijo aprendió en el cuarto grado y para ayudar a su hijo a prepararse para el año que viene. Las actividades están basadas en los Estándares comunes del estado (*Common Core State Standards*) y proveen práctica con las destrezas escenciales para el nivel de ese grado. Mantener a punto las destrezas que su hijo aprendió en el cuarto grado mientras su hijo está de descanso de la escuela ayudará a que el año del quinto grado comience de gran manera. También hay una sección al final del libro que provee práctica para los exámenes estandarizados.

Tenga en cuenta estos consejos mientras completa junto con su hijo el libro de *Kids Learn!*:

- Reserve **un tiempo específico todos los días** para trabajar en las actividades.
- **Complete una página de artes del lenguaje y una página de matemáticas** cada vez que su hijo trabaja con el libro, en lugar de completar al mismo tiempo las páginas de actividades que se completarían en una semana.
- Mantenga todas las **sesiones de práctica con su hijo positivas y constructivas.** Si el estado de ánimo se pone tenso, o usted o su hijo se frustran, ponga el libro a un lado y busque otro momento para la práctica.
- **Ayude a su hijo con las instrucciones,** si es necesario. Si a su hijo se le dificulta entender qué hacer, hagan algunos de los problemas juntos.
- Anime a su hijo a que haga su mejor esfuerzo y **elogie el empeño que se dedica cuando se aprende.** Celebre la terminación de todas las actividades llenando el certificado que se encuentra al final del libro y poniéndolo en un lugar especial.

Disfrute el tiempo en el que se aprende con su hijo durante sus vacaciones de la escuela. ¡El quinto grado llegará antes de que se dé cuenta!

Top 10 Things Your Fifth Grader Will Need to Know

1. **Identify themes** in books and stories

2. **Describe character development** and identify the conflict, climax, and resolution in a story

3. **Decode words** using root words, prefixes, and suffixes

4. Add and subtract equivalent **fractions** and **decimals** to hundredths

5. **Use long division** to divide large numbers by multi-digit numbers

6. **Ordered pairs and the coordinate plane** (*x*- and *y*-axis)

7. **Three major domains of life** (bacteria, archae, and eukaryota)

8. **Four states of matter** (solid, liquid, gas, and plasma)

9. **History of the United States** (American Indians, 13 colonies, American Revolution, and the Civil War)

10. **United States states and capitals**

#13537 Kids Learn! Getting Ready for 5th Grade

Las 10 cosas que su hijo de quinto grado debe saber

1. **Identificar temas** en libros y relatos

2. **Describir el desarrollo del personaje** e identificar el conflicto, el clímax y la resolución en un relato

3. **Desglosar palabras** utilizando raíces lingüísticas, prefijos y sufijos

4. Sumar y restar **fracciones** equivalentes y **decimales** a centenas

5. **Utilizar la división larga** para dividir números grandes por números de varias cifras

6. **Pares ordenados y plano de coordenadas** (*ejes "x" e "y"*)

7. **Los tres principales dominios de la vida** (bacteria, arquea y eucaria)

8. **Los cuatro estados de la materia** (sólido, líquido, gaseoso y plasma)

9. **Historia de los Estados Unidos** (indígenas americanos, las 13 colonias, la Revolución norteamericana y la guerra de Secesión)

10. **Los estados de Estados Unidos y sus capitales**

Things to Do at Home

To Develop Healthy Habits

- Allow your child to assume more responsibility at home. Give your child tasks, such as making his or her school lunch and helping with family chores.

- Post checklists and reminders to help your child establish good routines and stay organized.

- In order to guarantee a good night's sleep, make sure to eat dinner at least two hours before bedtime and ensure that your child goes to sleep at a consistent time each night. Children at this age need 10–11 hours of sleep per night, so plan ahead to make sure your child is well-rested.

To Practice Reading

- Send your child on a "print hunt." Challenge your child to find as many different kinds of print throughout the house as possible (e.g., labels, directions, maps).

- Have your child find four different types of advertisements in a magazine and identify the target audience for each one.

- After reading a short story or newspaper article, ask your child to retell the sequence of events using the words *first*, *next*, *then*, and *finally*.

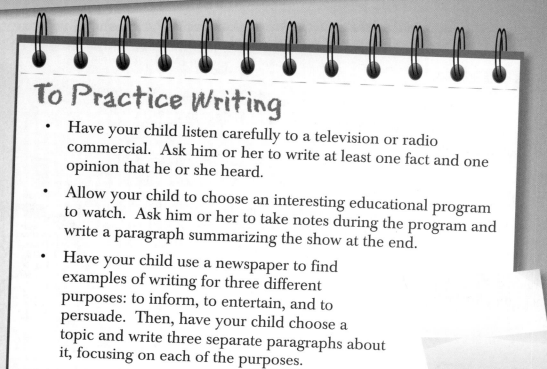

To Practice Writing

- Have your child listen carefully to a television or radio commercial. Ask him or her to write at least one fact and one opinion that he or she heard.

- Allow your child to choose an interesting educational program to watch. Ask him or her to take notes during the program and write a paragraph summarizing the show at the end.

- Have your child use a newspaper to find examples of writing for three different purposes: to inform, to entertain, and to persuade. Then, have your child choose a topic and write three separate paragraphs about it, focusing on each of the purposes.

To Practice Math

- Ask your child to calculate the area of his or her room. Then, challenge him or her to find the area of every room in your home and make a graph of the results.

- Have your child determine how long a container of laundry detergent will last based on how much detergent your family uses each week. Note the price of the detergent the next time you are at the store, then ask your child to calculate the cost per load of laundry.

- Help your child estimate the weight of various objects around the house. Then, show your child how to determine the actual weight of the object by weighing him- or herself both with and without the object and subtracting the difference.

Cosas para hacer en casa

Para desarrollar hábitos saludables

- Permita que su hijo asuma más responsabilidad en casa. Dé a su hijo tareas, como preparar el almuerzo para la escuela y ayudar con los quehaceres familiares.

- Pegue listas de cosas que hacer y recordatorios para ayudar a su hijo a establecer buenas rutinas y a continuar siendo organizado.

- Para garantizar un buen reposo por la noche, asegúrese de cenar al menos dos horas antes de la hora de dormir y asegúrese que su hijo se acueste a una hora consistente cada noche. Los niños de esta edad necesitan dormir de 10 a 11 horas todas las noches así que planee de antemano para que su hijo tenga un buen descanso.

Para practicar la lectura

- Mande a su hijo en una "búsqueda de letra impresa". Anime a su hijo a que encuentre tantos diferentes tipos de letra impresa por la casa como sea posible (p. ej. etiquetas, direcciones, mapas, etc.).

- Pida a su hijo que encuentre cuatro diferentes tipos de publicidad en una revista y que identifique el público meta para cada uno.

- Después de leer una historia corta o un artículo de revista, pídale a su hijo que vuelva a contar la secuencia de los acontecimientos usando las palabras *primero, después, luego* y *finalmente*.

Para practicar la escritura

- Pida a su hijo que escuche cuidadosamente un comercial de televisión o de radio. Pídale que escriba al menos un hecho y una opinión que escuchó.

- Permita a su hijo que escoja un interesante programa educativo. Pídale que tome notas durante el programa y que al final escriba un párrafo donde resume el programa.

- Pida a su hijo que use un periódico para encontrar ejemplos de escritura para tres propósitos: para informar, para entretener y para persuadir. Luego, pídale que escoja un tema y que escriba tres párrafos separados sobre el tema, enfocándose en cada uno de los propósitos.

Para practicar las matemáticas

- Pida a su hijo que calcule el área de su habitación. Luego, anímalo a que encuentre el área de cada cuarto de la casa y que haga una gráfica de los resultados.

- Pida a su hijo que determine qué tan grande es un contenedor de detergente para la ropa basándose en cuánto detergente usa su familia cada semana. Note el precio del detergente la próxima vez que vaya a la tienda, y luego pida a su hijo que calcule el costo de lavar cada canasta de ropa.

- Ayude a su hijo a calcular el peso de varios objetos en la casa. Luego muestre a su hijo cómo determinar el peso real del objeto al pesar a su hijo con y sin el objeto y restando la diferencia.

Things to Do in the Community

To Develop Good Citizenship

- Ask your child to write a poem, story, or song about what it means to be a good citizen. Have your child present his or her writing to a group of friends and neighbors.

- Help your child collect extra blankets or towels to donate to an animal shelter or rescue organization.

- Have your child think of a person in your community who exhibits good citizenship. Ask your child to write a thank-you note to honor that person's contributions to the community.

To Practice Reading

- On a trip to a new destination, have your child navigate by reading the map.

- Attend an event at your local public library. Many libraries have fun events for children, such as summer reading clubs, pajama story times in the evening, or story times in different languages.

- Have your child read the community section of the newspaper or a community newsletter. Ask him or her to select topics of interest to share with the family.

Things to Do in the Community *(cont.)*

To Practice Writing

- Ask your child to come up with ways to earn spending money and have him or her create an advertisement for his or her services to post in the community. Your child might offer babysitting, car washing, dog walking, or yard work services. Make sure your child includes rates, hours of availability, and a parent's contact information.

- Have your child visit a local fire station to obtain information about fire safety. Ask him or her to design and describe a fire evacuation plan for your family.

- Help your child create a family tree. Have him or her email or write letters to relatives to learn more about your family's ancestors and find missing information for the family tree.

To Practice Math

- Have your child compare gas prices at three different gas stations. Ask him or her to calculate the cost of filling up the car at each station.

- Obtain nutritional information sheets from local restaurants. Ask your child to calculate and compare the calorie totals for various combinations of food that he or she might want to eat there.

- Provide your child with a real or imaginary food budget for the week. Have him or her determine the average daily cost of feeding your family and then ask your child to select items at the grocery store that are the best value.

Cosas para hacer en la comunidad

Para ser un buen ciudadano

- Pida a su hijo que escriba un poema, historia o canción sobre qué significa ser un buen ciudadano. Pida a su hijo que presente su escrito a un grupo de amigos y vecinos.

- Ayude a su hijo a hacer una colecta de cobijas o toallas extras para donarlas a un albergue para animales o una sociedad protectora de animales.

- Pida a su hijo que piense de una persona en su comunidad que demuestra ser un buen ciudadano. Pida a su hijo que escriba una nota de agradecimiento para honrar las contribuciones de esa persona a la comunidad.

Para practicar la lectura

- Durante un viaje a un destino nuevo, pida a su hijo que dé direcciones leyendo el mapa.

- Asistan a un evento en su biblioteca pública local. Muchas bibliotecas tienen eventos divertidos para niños, como clubes de lectura de verano, horas de lectura en piyamas en la tarde o lecturas de cuentos en diferentes idiomas.

- Pida a su hijo que lea la sección de la comunidad del periódico o un boletín informativo comunitario. Pídale que escoja temas de interés para compartirlos con la familia.

Para practicar la escritura

- Pida a su hijo que idee maneras para ganar dinero de bolsillo y pídale que cree un anuncio con sus servicios para pegarlo en la comunidad. Su hijo puede ofrecer ser niñero, lavar carros, llevar a caminar perros o hacer trabajos en el patio. Asegúrese que su hijo incluya precios, horas de disponibilidad y los datos de un padre.

- Pida a su hijo que visite una estación de bomberos local para obtener información sobre la prevención de incendios. Pídale que diseñe y describa un plan de evacuación para su familia.

- Ayude a su hijo a crear un árbol genealógico. Pídale que envíe correos electrónicos o cartas a parientes para aprender más sobre los ancestros de su familia y para encontrar información faltante para el árbol genealógico.

Para practicar las matemáticas

- Pida a su hijo que compare los precios de la gasolina en tres diferentes gasolineras. Pídale que calcule el costo de llenar el tanque en cada gasolinera.

- Obtenga hojas de información nutricional de restaurantes locales. Pida a su hijo que calcule y compare las calorías totales para varias combinaciones de comida que él pueda querer comer ahí.

- Provea a su hijo de un presupuesto alimentario imaginario para la semana. Pídale que determine el costo promedio diario de alimentar a su familia y luego pídale que escoja artículos en el supermercado que tienen el mejor valor.

Suggested Vacation Reading
Lectura sugerida para las vacaciones

These books are recommended for students in fourth and fifth grades. Most, if not all, of these books are available at your local library or bookstore. Encourage your child to read daily and record his or her reading progress on the Vacation Reading Log on page 17.

Estos libros son recomendados para estudiantes de cuarto y quinto grado. La mayoría de estos libros, si no todos, están disponibles en su biblioteca local o librería. Anime a su hijo a que lea diariamente y registre el progreso de su lectura en el Registro de lectura de las vacaciones en la página 17.

Fiction

Hive Mind by Timothy J. Bradley
The Watsons Go to Birmingham—1963
  by Christopher Paul Curtis
Charlie and the Chocolate Factory by Roald Dahl
Number the Stars by Lois Lowry
Little House on the Prairie by Laura Ingalls Wilder
Brothers in Hope: The Story of the Lost Boys of Sudan
  by Mary Williams
Skylark by Patricia MacLachlan
Wayside School Is Falling Down by Louis Sachar
Little Cricket by Jackie Brown
Because of Winn-Dixie by Kate DiCamillo
Night of the Twisters by Ivy Ruckman

Nonfiction

Unsolved! History's Mysteries by Dona Herweck Rice
A Street Through Time by Anne Millard
Chuck Close: Face Book by Chuck Close
Haunted Histories: Creepy Castles, Dark Dungeons, and
  Powerful Palaces by J. H. Everett
Titanic: Voices from the Disaster by Deborah Hopkinson
A Gift of Days: The Greatest Words to Live By
  by Stephen Alcorn
Food Hates You, Too and Other Poems by Robert Weinstock
Lost Worlds by John Howe
Marching for Freedom: Walk Together Children and Don't You
  Grow Weary by Elizabeth Partridge
Mission Control, This is Apollo: The Story of the First Voyages
  to the Moon by Andrew Chaikin

#13537—Kids Learn! Getting Ready for 5th Grade

Vacation Reading Log
Registro de lectura de las vacaciones

Help your child complete this reading log to keep track of his or her vacation reading.
Ayude a su hijo a completar este registro de lectura para llevar la cuenta de su lectura durante las vacaciones.

Date *Fecha*	Title *Título*	Number of pages *Número de páginas*

Websites and Apps for Parents and Kids
Páginas web y aplicaciones para padres y niños

Language Arts Websites

Reading Rockets
http://www.readingrockets.org
Information, activities, and advice for parents

Book Adventure
http://www.bookadventure.com
Book quizzes for many different books

Read, Write, Think
http://www.readwritethink.org/parent-afterschool-resources
Student materials that support literacy learning in the K–12 classroom

International Children's Digital Library
http://en.childrenslibrary.org
Online database of eBooks organized by age, reading level, language, genre, or interest

ABCya.com
http://www.abcya.com
Online letter and number games and apps for children in grades K–5

Mathematics Websites

Math Playground
http://www.mathplayground.com
Collection of math games including numbers, word problems, logic, and manipulatives

Figure This! Math Challenges for Families
http://www.figurethis.org
Math problems to challenge families

Funbrain
http://www.funbrain.com/brain/MathBrain/MathBrain.html
Fun, arcade-style games covering a variety of math concepts

SoftSchools.com
http://www.softschools.com/math
Math concepts, tips, games, and activity sheets

Education.com
http://www.education.com/activity/math
Suggestions for math games to make and play at home

En español

Mundo Latino
http://www.mundolatino.org
Base de datos extensiva para hispanohablantes con enlaces a diferentes temas, juegos educativos y revistas en la red

StoryPlace
http://www.storyplace.org/sp/storyplace.asp
Una biblioteca digital con páginas llenas de cuentos para niños, jóvenes y adultos

¡Colorín Colorado!
http://www.colorincolorado.org
Información, actividades, y consejos para padres y maestros de estudiantes que hablan español

Aplicaciones Didácticas
http://www.aplicaciones.info/lectura/lectura.htm#peques
Base de datos de cuentos cortos y preguntas de comprensión correspondientes

Fun Educational Apps

Explor-eBook
Teacher Created Materials, Inc.
A library of hundreds of interactive eBook titles offers engaging reading practice across grade levels and content areas

Brain Quest® Blast Off
Modality, Inc.
Nearly 2,000 trivia questions from categories such as language arts, math, science, and social studies

Stack the States™
Freecloud Design, Inc.
A dynamic game that allows students to learn all about the 50 states

Slice It!
Com2uS USA, Inc.
Engaging puzzles that offer practice with fractions

Weekly Activities for Students
Actividades semanales para estudiantes

Comprehension Review: Stated Details

Directions: Read the passage, then answer the questions.

Instrucciones: Lee el pasaje, luego contesta las preguntas.

Sir Walter Raleigh was an English explorer, soldier, and writer in the late 1500s and early 1600s. He was also a good friend of Queen Elizabeth I of England. According to one story, Raleigh was once visiting the queen at her court. They were out walking. When they reached a large puddle, the queen stopped. Ever the gentleman, Raleigh took off his coat. He spread it on the ground so the queen could walk on it. He didn't want the queen to get her feet or clothes wet. No one knows if this story is true. We do know that Raleigh and the queen were friends. She made him a knight in 1585. She gave him a large piece **of** land in Ireland. He, in turn, helped the English defeat the Spanish at sea in 1588. He also sent colonists to North America in the 1580s. The two colonies founded on Roanoke Island in North America did not succeed.

Fluency Goal: Read 120 words in one minute. The bolded word is the 120th word in the passage.

Meta para la fluidez: Leer 120 palabras en un minuto. La palabra en negrita es la palabra número 120 en el pasaje.

1. Sir Walter Raleigh was a friend of Queen ____.

(A) Mary

(B) Elizabeth I

(C) Anne

(D) Elaine

2. In ____, the queen made Raleigh a knight.

(A) 1580

(B) 1585

(C) 1588

(D) 1590

3. According to one story, Raleigh took off his coat so that ____.

(A) the queen could walk on it

(B) he could use it as a pillow

(C) he wouldn't be hot

(D) the queen could wear it

4. Raleigh did not succeed in setting up colonies in ____.

(A) England

(B) Spain

(C) North America

(D) Ireland

#13537—Kids Learn! Getting Ready for 5th Grade

Comparing Quantities: What Multiplication Means

Directions: Draw a picture to represent the two quantities. Write two sentences to explain each comparison.

Instrucciones: *Haz un dibujo para representar las dos cantidades. Escribe dos oraciones para explicar cada comparación.*

Tip

A multiplication number sentence can be read as a comparison between the numbers in the equation.

Una oración numérica de multiplicación se puede leer como una comparación entre los números en la ecuación.

$4 \times 4 = 16$

4×4 is the same as 16.

16 is the same as 4×4.

16 is the same as 4 sets of 4.

16 is the same as 4 times 4.

$4 \times 4 = 16$

4×4 es lo mismo que 16.

16 es lo mismo que 4×4.

16 es lo mismo que 4 grupos of 4.

16 es lo mismo que 4 veces 4.

1. $3 \times 9 = 27$

2. $5 \times 6 = 30$

$3 \times 9 = 27$

4×3 is the same as 27

27 is the same as

3 sets of 9

27 is the same

as 3×9

$5 \times 6 = 30$.

6×5 is the same as

30. is the same as 5 sets of

6.

30 is the same as

5×6.

Explicit vs. Implicit Details

Directions: Decide whether each item gives you explicit information or whether you have to make an inference based on implicit details. Write *explicit* or *implicit* on the lines provided.

Instrucciones: *Decide si cada objeto te da información explícita o si tienes que hacer una deducción basada en detalles implícitos. Escribe* explícito *o* implícito *en las líneas provistas.*

Explicit information is very clear and easy to understand. *Implicit information* is not as clear and easy to recognize; a reader must make an *inference* about what is actually happening.

La información explícita *es muy clara y fácil de reconocer. La* información implícita *no es tan clara y fácil de reconocer; un lector tiene que hacer una* deducción *sobre qué es lo que ocurre realmente.*

1. The woman wore her new red dress to the fundraiser. She saw many friends that she knew and was excited to have a good time.

   explicit

2. Grace was ready for the bell to ring. She was so excited. Cake, balloons, presents, and dinner out at a restaurant—it was going to be a great night!

   Implicit

3. Manuel only got halfway home on his bike. He was so frustrated. It was still a long walk. He took one more look at the tire and then just started walking, feeling sorry for himself.

   explicit

4. Many of the reasons that plants and animals are endangered are due to the actions of human beings. Pollution is one of the main reasons that living things are struggling to survive.

   explicit

5. It is Emily's favorite time to be outside and look up at the sky. The rain stops and the sun comes out. Then, as if a painter creates it in the sky, a beautiful scene emerges through the clouds.

   explicit

Addition and Subtraction Word Problems

Directions: Solve the problems. Circle the important facts you need to solve them.

Instrucciones: *Soluciona los problemas. Encierra con un círculo los datos importantes que necesitas para resolverlos. Usa el espacio provisto para mostrar tu trabajo.*

1. There were 76 students in a school jog-a-thon. Twenty-six of them were in 3rd grade, 28 of them were in 4th grade, and 22 of them were in 5th grade.

   a. How many 4th- and 5th-grade students were in the jog-a-thon? _____ 50

   b. Which grade had the most students in the jog-a-thon? ___4th grade___

   28
   22 +
   50

2. The jog-a-thon route covered 150 kilometers. There were 4 rest stops for the runners. Niki ran 52 kilometers and stopped at the second rest stop.

   a. How much farther does Niki have to run to complete the route? ___48 kilometers___

   b. Has she gone at least half the distance? ___No___

   52

3. Melita's team wanted to collect a total of $325.00. They collected $208.75 from the jog-a-thon and $76.20 from a candy sale.

   208.75
   76.20 +
   284.95

   a. How much money did they collect? ___284.95___

   b. Would they collect more money from 3 candy sales than from 1 jog-a-thon?

   ___3 candy sales is more___

   76.20   152.40
   76.20 +   76.20 +
   152.40   228.60

4. Twenty team members had lunch together at the third rest stop. They had traveled 70 kilometers. Thirteen team members drank milk with their lunch and the rest drank grape juice.

   20
   13 -
   7

   a. How many team members drank grape juice? ___7___

   b. How many team members did not drink grape juice? ___13___

A Visit with Penguins

Directions: Read the passage, then answer the questions.

Instrucciones: *Lee el pasaje, luego contesta las preguntas.*

One of the penguins was ready to play. He waddled up the icy hill as fast as he could. Then, he flopped onto his stomach and slid down. Some of the penguins were eating lunch. They swallowed the fish as quickly as the zookeeper could empty the big buckets of food. A few of the penguins were sleeping quietly.

The children watched the penguins for a long time. When it was time to leave the exhibit, all the children were sad to go. Many of the children liked the penguin exhibit best.

1. Write 1–2 sentences to summarize the passage.

Kids were seeing the exbit they saw penquins slide done a icy hill and swallowed the whin the Bucket droped down. Many people liked liked it and did not want to go back home

2. What do you think will happen next? Why?

I think the Penquins will play around and doesnt care about anybody and keeps on playing.

#13537—Kids Learn! Getting Ready for 5th Grade

Fraction Solutions

Directions: Write each improper fraction as a multiplication expression and as words. Draw a picture to show the amount.

Instrucciones: *Escribe cada fracción impropia como una expresión de multiplicación y como palabras. Haz un dibujo para mostrar la cantidad.*

Tip

An *improper fraction* has a numerator that is greater than (or equal to) the denominator.

$\frac{3}{2}$, $\frac{6}{3}$, and $\frac{9}{2}$ are all improper fractions.

$\frac{3}{2}$ is an improper fraction that can also be thought of as *three halves*.

Una fracción impropia *tiene un numerador que es más grande que (o igual a) el denominador.*

$\frac{3}{2}$, $\frac{6}{3}$, *y* $\frac{9}{2}$ *son todas fracciones impropias.*

$\frac{3}{2}$ *es una fracción impropia que también se puede entender como* tres mitades.

$\frac{3}{2} = 3 \times \frac{1}{2}$

---

1. $\frac{6}{4} = \underline{6} \times \underline{\frac{1}{4}}$ Picture:

2. $\frac{8}{5} = \underline{9} \times \underline{\frac{1}{5}}$ Picture:

$8 \times \frac{1}{5}$

3. $\frac{5}{3} = \underline{5} \times \underline{\frac{1}{3}}$ Picture:

Define It

Directions: Look up the meaning of each word in an online dictionary (for example, www.m-w.com). Record the definition of each word, then make up a new sentence using each word.

Instrucciones: *Busca el significado de cada palabra en un diccionario en línea (por ejemplo, www.m-w.com). Registra la definición de cada palabra, luego inventa una nueva oración usando cada palabra.*

1. Mei-yin couldn't <u>coax</u> her friend into riding the roller coaster with her.

Definition: _coax means cling_

Sentence: _my sister always clings me_

2. My favorite time of day to visit the beach is at <u>dusk</u>.

Definition: _before night_

Sentence: _Before night I see t.v_

3. The hikers were <u>weary</u> after a long day of climbing through the mountains.

Definition: _tired_

Sentence: _I get tired by walking outside_

4. There was a <u>considerable</u> amount of water on the road after the heavy rain.

Definition: _amout_

Sentence: _I 3s a mout of water_

Sign In

Directions: Place + and − signs in the boxes so that both sides of each equation are equal.

Instrucciones: Coloca signos de + y − en los cuadros para que ambos lados de la ecuación sean iguales.

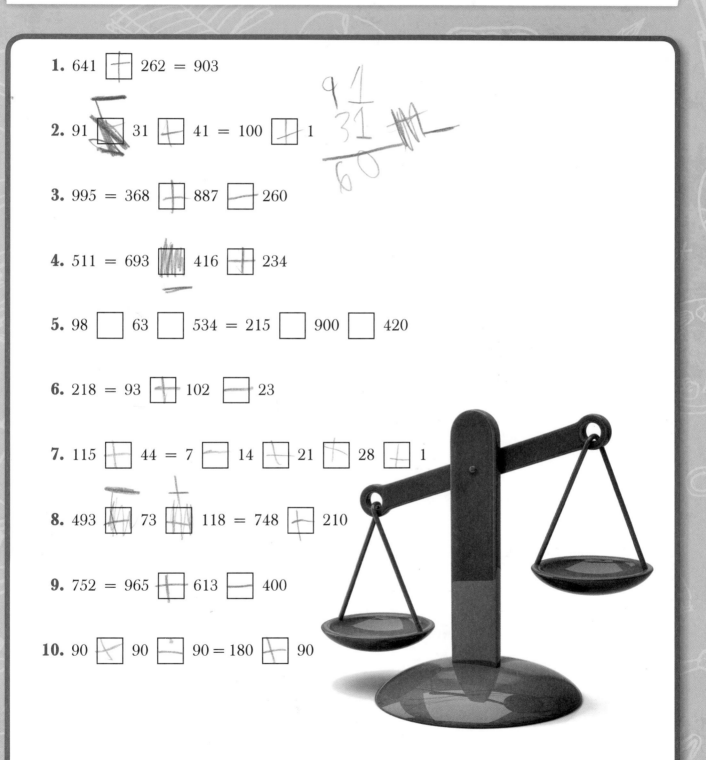

1. 641 ☐ 262 = 903

2. 91 ☐ 31 ☐ 41 = 100 ☐ 1

3. 995 = 368 ☐ 887 ☐ 260

4. 511 = 693 ☐ 416 ☐ 234

5. 98 ☐ 63 ☐ 534 = 215 ☐ 900 ☐ 420

6. 218 = 93 ☐ 102 ☐ 23

7. 115 ☐ 44 = 7 ☐ 14 ☐ 21 ☐ 28 ☐ 1

8. 493 ☐ 73 ☐ 118 = 748 ☐ 210

9. 752 = 965 ☐ 613 ☐ 400

10. 90 ☐ 90 ☐ 90 = 180 ☐ 90

Complete the Sentences

Directions: Complete the sentences. Be sure to add punctuation at the end.

Instrucciones: *Completa las oraciones. Asegúrate de agregar la puntuación al final.*

Tip

Every sentence must have a *subject* and a *predicate*. The subject is what or whom the sentence is about. The predicate tells something about the subject. The predicate always includes a verb.

Cada oración debe tener un sujeto y un predicado. El sujeto es sobre quién o qué trata el enunciado. El predicado dice algo sobre el sujeto. El predicado siempre incluye un verbo.

1. Sandy cried when she ___brocke the glass while running___

2. The best place in the world to ___live in is usa___

3. Who can ___be the best scientist___

4. I wish I had ___a robot that does work___

5. There aren't many ___monkeys around the___

6. This is the best ___world day of my life___

7. It's times like this that _____

8. When are you going to ___scholl it is hard___

Subtraction Solutions

Directions: Solve the subtraction problems. Then, fill in the puzzle with the word form of each answer.

Instrucciones: *Resuelve los problemas de restas. Luego, llena el rompecabezas con la respuesta escrita en forma de palabra.*

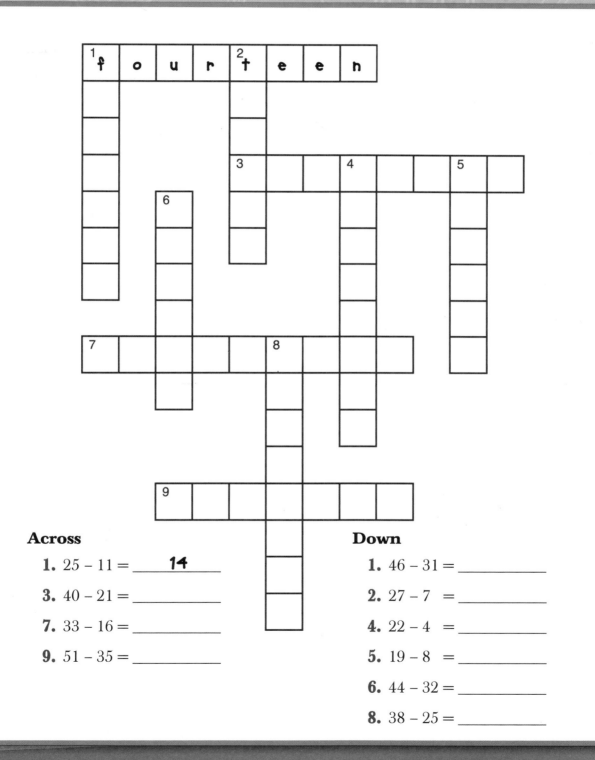

Across

1. $25 - 11 =$ ___14___

3. $40 - 21 =$ _____

7. $33 - 16 =$ _____

9. $51 - 35 =$ _____

Down

1. $46 - 31 =$ _____

2. $27 - 7 =$ _____

4. $22 - 4 =$ _____

5. $19 - 8 =$ _____

6. $44 - 32 =$ _____

8. $38 - 25 =$ _____

What's Your Opinion?

Directions: Choose a topic that is important to you. Plan an opinion piece using the outline below. Then, use the outline to write your opinion piece on another sheet of paper.

Instrucciones: *Escoge un tema que sea importante para ti. Planea un artículo de opinión usando el borrador de abajo. Luego, usa el borrador para escribir tu opinión en otra hoja de papel.*

An *opinion piece* is a way to share your own point of view in writing. Writers must support their views with facts and details.

Un artículo de opinión *es una manera de compartir tu punto de vista por escrito. Los escritores deben de apoyar su punto de vista con hechos y detalles.*

Topic: food

Opinion: I like to eat food

Fact #1: _____

    Detail #1: _____

    Detail #2: _____

Fact #2: _____

    Detail #1: _____

    Detail #2: _____

Fact #3: _____

    Detail #1: _____

    Detail #2: _____

Conclusion: _____

Reading Comprehension

Directions: Read the passage, then answer the questions.

Instrucciones: *Lee el pasaje, luego contesta las preguntas.*

The tribe had but one problem—a steady supply of fresh water. Everyone needed water for drinking, cooking, and cleaning. Yet the nearby stream to which the women carried their water jugs each day would sometimes abruptly stop flowing. There was neither rhyme nor reason to the dry spells. No one could predict them, for there was never any warning. Sometimes the problem lasted for days, other times for weeks. Whenever it happened, the women of the tribe had to spend most of their day walking to and from a distant pool. Nobody actually knew why this kept happening.

On the day our story begins, the women took their water jugs to fill them. When they reached the stream, **however**, they found it all but empty. Shallow depressions held small, muddy puddles of water, but even those would disappear under the sun's scorching rays. The women split into two groups. One group followed the stream to see if any water could be found farther downstream. The other followed the stream to look for water upstream. But just as every time before, none could be found anywhere.

Fluency Goal: Read 120 words in one minute. The bolded word is the 120th word in the passage.

Meta para la fluidez: Leer 120 palabras en un minuto. La palabra en negrita es la palabra número 120 en el pasaje.

1. What is the main idea?

 A Sometimes the stream is dry, but nobody knows why.

B A magic spell has been placed on the stream that the tribe relies upon for water.

C The women of the tribe must carry water to the village.

 D The tribe can never get enough water from a nearby stream.

2. Which is the best title for this passage?

A A Tribe with a Problem

B The Mysterious Stream

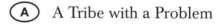 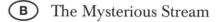 **C** The Thirsty Tribe

D Muddy Water Misery

Calculating Area

Directions: Compute the area of each rectangle.

Instrucciones: *Calcula el área de cada rectángulo.*

Tip

To compute the area of a rectangle, multiply the length by the width.

- Area = length × width
- $A = l \times w$

Para calcular el área de un rectángulo, multiplica lo largo por lo ancho.

- *Área = largo × ancho*
- $A = l \times a$

18 ft.

7 ft.

$A = 18 \times 7$

$A = 126$ square feet (126 ft.^{2})

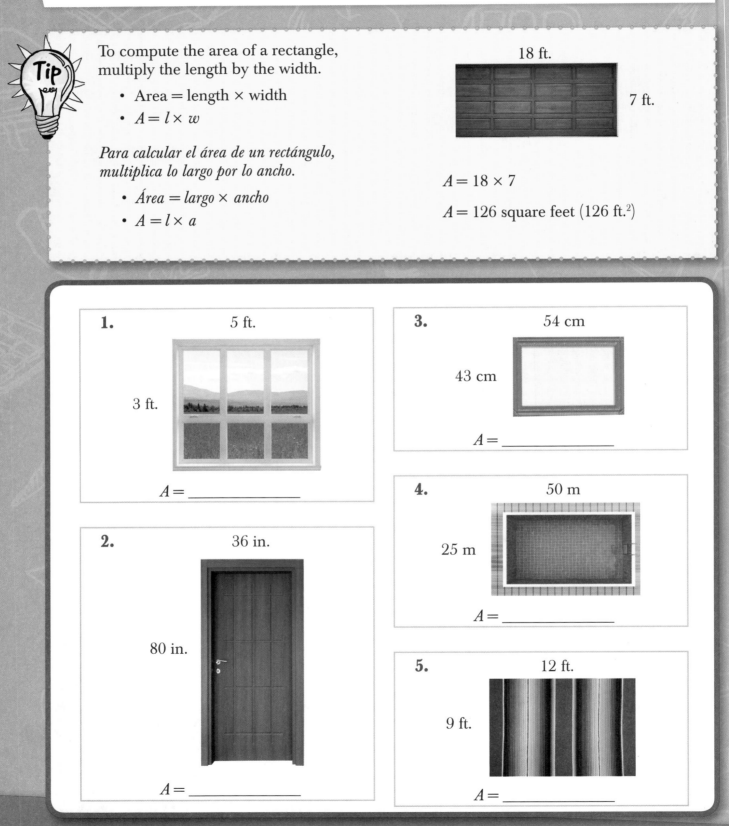

1.   5 ft.

3 ft.

$A =$ _____

2.   36 in.

80 in.

$A =$ _____

3.   54 cm

43 cm

$A =$ _____

4.   50 m

25 m

$A =$ _____

5.   12 ft.

9 ft.

$A =$ _____

Nonfiction Reading Journal

Directions: Choose nonfiction material to read from a book, a newspaper, or a magazine. Before reading, fill out the first two sections below. After reading, complete the last two sections.

Instrucciones: Escoge material de lectura de no ficción de un libro, un periódico o una revista. Antes de leer, llena las primeras dos secciones de abajo. Después de leer, completa las últimas dos secciones.

Topic: _____

Source: _____

Pages: _____

Before Reading

I know the following facts about this topic:

1. _____
2. _____
3. _____

I have the following questions about this topic:

1. _____
2. _____
3. _____

After Reading

I learned the following new facts about this topic:

1. _____
2. _____
3. _____

I would like to learn more about: _____

_____

_____

Line Them Up: Making Line Plots

Directions: Use the data below to make a line plot. Then, answer the questions.

Instrucciones: *Usa la información a continuación para hacer un diagrama de puntos. Luego, contesta las preguntas.*

Tip

A *line plot* shows data on a number line with various symbols to show frequency, such as an *x*. An *x* is marked each time the same measurement appears. A line plot makes it easy to see which measurements appear most or least often.

Un diagrama de puntos muestra información en una línea numérica con varios símbolos para mostrar frecuencia, tal como una x. Se marca una x cada vez que aparece la misma medición. Un diagrama de puntos hace que sea fácil ver cuales mediciones aparecen más o menos frecuentemente.

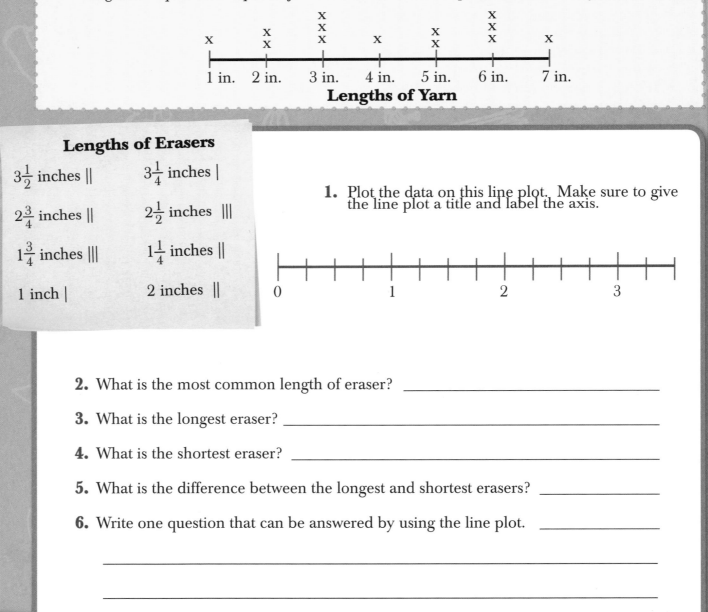

Lengths of Yarn

Lengths of Erasers

$3\frac{1}{2}$ inches || $3\frac{1}{4}$ inches |

$2\frac{3}{4}$ inches || $2\frac{1}{2}$ inches |||

$1\frac{3}{4}$ inches ||| $1\frac{1}{4}$ inches ||

1 inch | 2 inches ||

1. Plot the data on this line plot. Make sure to give the line plot a title and label the axis.

2. What is the most common length of eraser? _____

3. What is the longest eraser? _____

4. What is the shortest eraser? _____

5. What is the difference between the longest and shortest erasers? _____

6. Write one question that can be answered by using the line plot. _____

_____

_____

Main Idea

Directions: Read the paragraph below and use the guide to help you determine the main idea.

Instrucciones: *Lee el párrafo a continuación y usa la guía para ayudarte a determinar la idea principal.*

Tip

To determine the main idea of a paragraph, read the paragraph carefully and answer the three *W*s (who, what, and why). Then, use the answers to these questions to determine the main idea.

Para determinar la idea principal de un párrafo, lee el párrafo cuidadosamente y contesta las tres Qs (quién, qué y por qué). Luego, usa las respuestas a estas preguntas para determinar la idea principal.

Lola loved to watch the big, beautiful birds from South America. She stared at the parrots' bright blue wings as the birds flew gracefully in their giant bird cage. Lola laughed when they called to each other with loud, squeaky voices. The parrots were Lola's favorite animals at the zoo.

1. Who? _____

2. What? _____

3. Why? _____

4. Write a sentence that tells the main idea using your answers: _____

_____

_____

Multiplication Practice

Directions: Find each product.

Instrucciones: *Encuentra cada producto.*

1.
$$\begin{array}{r} 53 \\ \times\, 54 \\ \hline \mathbf{212} \\ \mathbf{+2650} \\ \hline \mathbf{2,862} \end{array}$$

2.
$$\begin{array}{r} 25 \\ \times\, 36 \\ \hline \end{array}$$

3.
$$\begin{array}{r} 36 \\ \times\, 72 \\ \hline \end{array}$$

4.
$$\begin{array}{r} 49 \\ \times\, 23 \\ \hline \end{array}$$

5.
$$\begin{array}{r} 54 \\ \times\, 23 \\ \hline \end{array}$$

6.
$$\begin{array}{r} 76 \\ \times\, 53 \\ \hline \end{array}$$

7.
$$\begin{array}{r} 67 \\ \times\, 29 \\ \hline \end{array}$$

8.
$$\begin{array}{r} 45 \\ \times\, 78 \\ \hline \end{array}$$

Adjectives and Adverbs

Directions: Add adjectives and adverbs to the following sentences to make them more specific and interesting. Then, reread your sentences to make sure the adjectives are ordered correctly in each sentence.

Instrucciones: *Agrega adjetivos y adverbios a las siguientes oraciones para que sean más específicas e interesantes. Luego, relee tus oraciones para asegurarte que los adjetivos están en el orden correcto en cada oración.*

Adjectives are used to modify nouns and pronouns. *Adverbs* are used to modify verbs, adjectives, and other adverbs. Both are used to make writing more specific and interesting.

Los adjetivos *se usan para modificar los sustantivos y pronombres. Los* adverbios *se usan para modificar los verbos, adjetivos y otros adverbios. Ambos se usan para hacer la escritura más específica e interesante.*

Example without adjectives and adverbs: The convertible ran into the truck.

Example with adjectives and adverbs: The **red, shiny Mustang convertible suddenly** ran into the **four-door, white Dodge pickup** truck.

1. The dog barked at the cat. _____

_____

2. The clown entertained the crowd. _____

_____

3. I hit the ball. _____

_____

4. Mei Ling ate lunch. _____

_____

5. Everyone watched Rafael play basketball. _____

_____

Protractor Pro

Directions: Use a protractor to measure the angles below. Then, write whether the angle is a right angle, an acute angle, or an obtuse angle.

Instrucciones: *Usa un transportador para medir los ángulos de abajo. Luego, escribe si el ángulo es un ángulo recto, un ángulo agudo o un ángulo obtuso.*

> A *right angle* measures 90°. Any angle less than a right angle is an *acute angle*. Any angle greater than a right angle and less than a straight angle is called an *obtuse angle*.
>
> *Un ángulo recto mide 90°. Cualquier ángulo menor que un ángulo recto es un ángulo agudo. Cualquier ángulo mayor que un ángulo recto y menor que un ángulo llano se llama ángulo obtuso.*

right angle	acute angle	obtuse angle
ángulo recto	*ángulo agudo*	*ángulo obtuso*

1.

The angle is _____°.

It is a(n) _____ angle.

2.

The angle is _____°.

It is a(n) _____ angle.

3.

The angle is _____°.

It is a(n) _____ angle.

4.

The angle is _____°.

It is a(n) _____ angle.

Sentence Emergencies

Directions: These sentences need your help! Be a sentence doctor and fix these sentences. Rewrite the sentences using correct capitalization and punctuation.

Instrucciones: *¡Estas oraciones necesitan tu ayuda! Juega al médico de oraciones y arregla estas oraciones. Reescribe las oraciones usando las mayúsculas y la puntuación correctas.*

1. yes we go to the library on Tuesdays

   Yes, we go to the library on Tuesdays.

2. mrs smith is your teacher

3. the students in mr garcias class were reading charlottes web

4. what a wonderful day it is

5. jordan come play with us in griffith park

6. watch out michelle

7. maria what is your favorite kind of math problem

8. i will paint johns room today

Pieces of the Pie

Directions: Draw a picture to solve each problem. Write your answer on the line.

Instrucciones: *Haz un dibujo para resolver cada problema. Escribe tu respuesta en la línea.*

Tip

Imagine that a pie is cut into 8 equal slices. Joe ate 3 slices. Leilani ate 2 slices. Add the fractions to determine how much pie was eaten. Keep the denominators the same and add the numerators.

Imagina que se corta una tarta en 8 pedazos iguales. Joe comió 3 pedazos. Leilani comió 2 pedazos. Suma las fracciones para determinar cuánta tarta se comió. Manten los denominadores iguales y suma los numeradores.

$$\frac{3}{8} + \frac{2}{8} = \frac{5}{8}$$

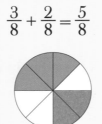

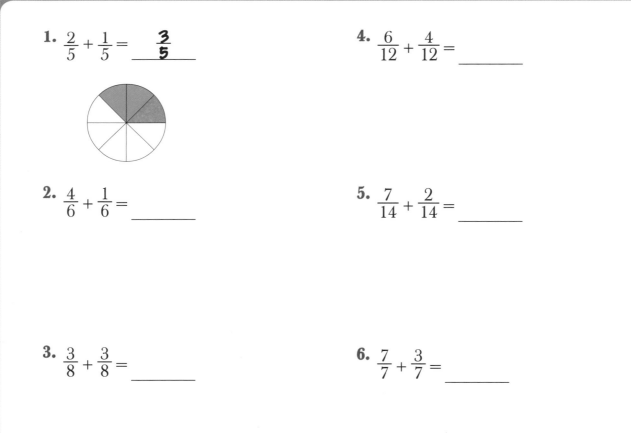

1. $\frac{2}{5} + \frac{1}{5} =$ **$\frac{3}{5}$**

2. $\frac{4}{6} + \frac{1}{6} =$ _____

3. $\frac{3}{8} + \frac{3}{8} =$ _____

4. $\frac{6}{12} + \frac{4}{12} =$ _____

5. $\frac{7}{14} + \frac{2}{14} =$ _____

6. $\frac{7}{7} + \frac{3}{7} =$ _____

Circus Balloon

Directions: Finish the story below. Include descriptive words in your story. Use the five senses (sight, sound, touch, taste, and smell) to add details.

Instrucciones: *Termina la historia a continuación. Incluye palabras descriptivas en tu historia. Usa los cinco sentidos (vista, oído, tacto, sabor y olor) para agregar detalles.*

A man from the circus filled the boy's large, red balloon with helium and tied it to a long ribbon. The boy held the ribbon tightly in his hand and walked over to see the enormous, gray elephant. All of a sudden, a brisk wind . . .

_____

_____

_____

_____

_____

_____

_____

_____

_____

_____

_____

_____

_____

_____

_____

Tia and the Bully

Directions: Read the passage, then answer the questions.

Instrucciones: *Lee el pasaje, luego contesta las preguntas.*

Tia was 11, but very small for her age. Everyone in her family was tall. Tia wished someday soon she would be tall, too.

One of the girls at Tia's school liked to pick on her. She would take food from Tia's lunch and eat it. She would break Tia's pencils and tear up her homework. She would get other kids to tease Tia, too. Tia never told the teacher or her parents about the bully. She was too ashamed.

That summer, Tia grew and grew. When she went back to school, she was the tallest girl in her class. She was even taller than the bully. She could have taken the bully's lunch and eaten it. She could have broken her pencils and torn up her homework. But Tia didn't do any of those things. When her friends asked her why, she simply replied, "Because even though I'm bigger than she is now, I don't ever want to be a bully."

Over time, the bully felt bad about what she had done. She asked Tia to forgive her. Soon, the girls became good friends.

One day, a new girl came into class. She didn't like Tia's friend and soon began to bully her. She did the same things that the bully had done to Tia. Tia could have let her do those things to her new friend. She could have thought, "Let her see how it feels to be bullied like she did to me." Instead, Tia told the new girl to stop picking on her friend. The new girl was afraid of Tia, so she stopped what she was doing.

When Tia's friend found out what she had done for her, she felt happy to have a friend like Tia. And Tia was happy to be a friend instead of a bully.

1. What did Tia do when the bully bullied her? _____

_____

2. Did Tia bully anyone else? Why or why not? _____

_____

3. How did Tia get the new bully to stop bullying her friend? _____

_____

4. How could the story have ended differently? _____

_____

Divide It!

Directions: Find the quotients.

Instrucciones: *Encuentra los cocientes.*

> 💡 **Tip**
>
> There are several strategies for solving division problems, including the *rectangle sections (or box) method*, *expanded notation method*, and the *digit-by-digit (traditional) method*. Search the Internet for examples of these different methods, and practice them with these problems.
>
> *Hay varias estrategias para resolver problemas de división, como el método de secciones de rectángulo (o de caja), el método de notación extendida y el método de dígito por dígito (tradicional). Busca en Internet ejemplos de estos métodos diferentes y practícalos con estos problemas.*

1. $9\overline{)5,421}$

$$600 + 2 = 602\ R3$$

9	5,421	21
	-5400	-18

21   3 ← remainder

2. $3\overline{)3,653}$

3. $4\overline{)6,011}$

4. $8\overline{)6,476}$

5. $3\overline{)2,937}$

6. $6\overline{)7,265}$

7. $9\overline{)4,518}$

8. $2\overline{)4,048}$

9. $7\overline{)8,109}$

Put Them in Order

Directions: Read the sentences. Rewrite them in a paragraph in the correct sequence using time-order words (e.g., *first, next, then, last*) to help the structure of the narrative. Then, write another paragraph to continue the story.

Instrucciones: *Lee las oraciones. Reescríbelas en un párrafo en el orden correcto usando palabras de tiempo y orden (p. ej.,* primero, después, luego, último*) para ayudar a la estructura de la narrativa. Luego, escribe otro párrafo para continuar la histora.*

- I got out of bed and looked in the mirror.

- I ran to my mother to show her what had happened.

- She said, "It appears that those seeds you swallowed yesterday have been planted inside you."

- I woke up one morning feeling strange.

- Then, she looked in the phone book for a good gardener to come over to trim me.

- What a shock I got when I saw a plant growing out of my ears!

- I am feeling better now, but I still have to water myself every day.

44

#13537—Kids Learn! Getting Ready for 5th Grade

© Teacher Created Materials

Number Round-Up

Directions: Round each number to the specified places.

Instrucciones: *Redondea cada número a los lugares especificados.*

Tip

When rounding to the nearest ten, check the number in the ones place.
Cuando redondeas a la decena, revisa el número de las unidades.

If the number is 5 or greater, round up. **Example:** 4<u>7</u> → 50

If the number is 4 or less, round down. **Example:** 4<u>3</u> → 40

Si el número es mayor que 5, redondea aumentando. ***Ejemplo:*** *4<u>7</u> → 50*

Si el número es menor que 4, redondea reduciendo. ***Ejemplo:*** *4<u>3</u> → 40*

When rounding to the nearest hundred, check the number in the tens place.
Cuando redondeas a la centena, revisa el número en el lugar de las decenas.

If the number is 5 or greater, round up. **Example:** 1<u>5</u>8 → 200

If the number is 4 or less, round down. **Example:** 1<u>3</u>2 → 100

Si el número es mayor que 5, redondea aumentando. ***Ejemplo:*** *1<u>5</u>8 → 200*

Si el número es menor que 4, redondea reduciendo. ***Ejemplo:*** *1<u>3</u>2 → 100*

When rounding to the nearest thousand, check the number in the hundreds place.
Cuando redondeas al millar, revisa el número en el lugar de las centenas.

If the number is 5 or greater, round up. **Example:** 1,<u>9</u>03 → 2,000

If the number is 4 or less, round down. **Example:** 1,<u>4</u>99 → 1,000

Si el número es mayor que 5, redondea aumentando. ***Ejemplo:*** *1,<u>9</u>03 → 2,000*

Si el número es menor que 4, redondea reduciendo. ***Ejemplo:*** *1,<u>4</u>99 → 1,000*

1. 6,409

Rounded to the nearest thousand:

_____

Rounded to the nearest hundred:

_____

Rounded to the nearest ten: _____

2. 7,516

Rounded to the nearest thousand:

_____

Rounded to the nearest hundred:

_____

Rounded to the nearest ten: _____

3. 3,099

Rounded to the nearest thousand:

_____

Rounded to the nearest hundred:

_____

Rounded to the nearest ten: _____

4. Explain a real-life situation in which you would use rounding.

_____

_____

_____

_____

What's the Word?

Directions: Use an online thesaurus to find synonyms and antonyms for each of the words. Then, write a sentence using one of the synonyms.

Instrucciones: Usa un tesauro para encontrar sinónimos y antónimos para cada una de las palabras. Luego, escribe una oración usando uno de los sinónimos.

1. happiness

Synonyms: _____

Antonyms: _____

Synonym Sentence: _____

2. anger

Synonyms: _____

Antonyms: _____

Synonym Sentence: _____

3. great

Synonyms: _____

Antonyms: _____

Synonym Sentence: _____

4. hot

Synonyms: _____

Antonyms: _____

Synonym Sentence: _____

Compare Them!

Directions: Decide whether the first number is greater than, less than, or equal to the second number. Use the >, <, and = symbols to compare the numbers.

Instrucciones: *Decide si el primer número es mayor que, menor que o igual al segundo número. Usa los signos >, <, = para comparar los números.*

1. 802 ◯ 820

2. 4,105 ◯ 5,104

3. 8,001 ◯ 8,001

4. 165,318 ◯ 65,318

5. 7,772 ◯ 7,782

6. 90,176 ◯ 89,176

7. 376,345 ◯ 3,376,345

8. 499,901 ◯ 499,109

9. 2,618,002 ◯ 2,718,001

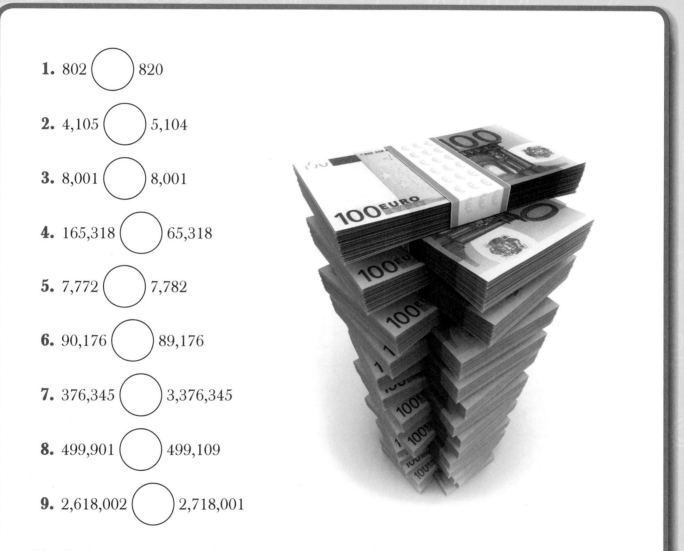

10. Explain your strategy for comparing two numbers.

_____

_____

_____

Specific Details

Directions: Read the paragraph below. Cross out the sentences that do not support the topic sentence of this paragraph. Then, rewrite the edited paragraph on the lines below.

Instrucciones: *Lee el párrafo a continuación. Tacha las oraciones que no apoyan la oración principal de este párrafo. Luego, reescribe el párrafo editado en las líneas de abajo.*

Camping Is Fun

Camping is fun for many reasons. It is fun to be out in the wilderness, far away from the cares of everyday life. I don't have to worry about things like chores and homework. I got a good grade on my last homework assignment, though. Even though there are camping chores I must do, somehow they are duties I look forward to. Last week at school I had hall duty. I enjoy building a campfire and keeping it going. Our home fireplace uses gas. If we are camping near a lake or stream, I can go fishing, one of my favorite pastimes. I can't remember whether I put plenty of food in my fish tank at home. There is nothing better than freshly caught fish cooked over an open campfire. My mother says that the fish at our local market do not always seem fresh to her. Yes, give me a camp in the woods, a roaring campfire, and fish to catch and eat, and I am truly a happy camper.

Comparing the Places of Value

Directions: Solve each problem.

Instrucciones: *Resuelve cada problema.*

Place value refers to the value of the place that a digit occupies in a number. Each place is ten times larger than the place to its right.

El valor de posición *se refiere al valor del lugar que ocupa un dígito en un número. Cada lugar es diez veces mayor que el lugar a su derecha.*

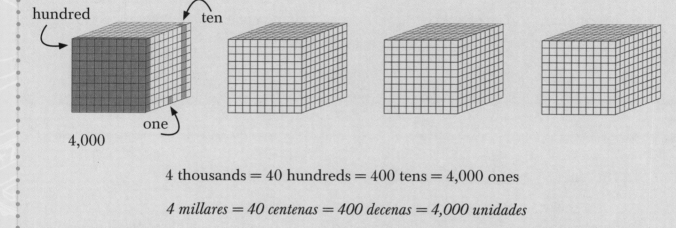

hundred   ten

one

4,000

4 thousands = 40 hundreds = 400 tens = 4,000 ones

4 millares = 40 centenas = 400 decenas = 4,000 unidades

1. ___**5**___ thousands = 50 hundreds. Write the number: _____**5,000**_____

2. _____ hundreds = 60 tens. Write the number: _____

3. _____ ones = 2 tens. Write the number: _____

4. _____ tens = 27 hundreds. Write the number: _____

5. _____ thousands = 356 hundreds. Write the number: _____

6. _____ ones = 87 hundreds. Write the number: _____

7. _____ thousands = 710 tens. Write the number: _____

8. _____ ones = 910 hundreds. Write the number: _____

It's All Relative!

Directions: Complete the following sentences with the correct relative pronoun.

Instrucciones: *Completa las oraciones siguientes con el pronombre relativo correcto.*

> **Tip**
>
> A *pronoun* is a word that replaces a noun, such as *he, me,* or *we.*
>
> A *relative pronoun* introduces a *relative clause.*
>
> There are five relative pronouns: *that, which, who, whom,* and *whose.*
>
> *Un* pronombre *es una palabra que toma el lugar de un sustantivo, como* él, yo *o* nosotros.
>
> *Un* pronombre relativo *introduce una* cláusula de relativo.
>
> *Hay cinco pronombres relativos en inglés:* that, which, who, whom *y* whose.

1. The letter _____ you gave me was very thoughtful and kind.

2. Babe Ruth, _____ is still considered one of the greatest athletes in all of American sports, will never be forgotten.

3. A fifth grader, _____ main job is to work hard in school, is still learning how to be responsible.

4. Ramona ordered the chocolate cake, _____ is why her sister made the same choice.

5. The library's children's section was full of students, almost all of _____ were looking for research books for their reports that are due on Friday.

6. My favorite pizza topping is pepperoni, _____ was the most popular response in the class survey.

USA 33

BABE RUTH

#13537—Kids Learn! Getting Ready for 5th Grade

Multistep Word Problems

Directions: Solve the problems. Show the steps you take to find the answer.

Instrucciones: *Resuelve los problemas. Muestra los pasos que tomas para encontrar la respuesta.*

1. Sergio enjoys collecting stamps as a hobby. He collected 12 stamps in June, 24 in July, and 29 in August. Then, he decided to give 18 to his brother. How many stamps does Sergio have left?

2. Lily ate three strawberries at breakfast and had two times that many for lunch. If she wants to eat 20 strawberries in one day, how many will she need to have for dessert?

3. A large pizza has 24 slices. If 7 friends want to share the pizza, and they each want 3 slices, is there enough pizza? If so, how much is left?

4. Parker made 75 cents at his lemonade stand on Saturday. He made two times as much as that on Sunday. Parker wants to buy two candy bars that cost $1.00 each. Does he have enough money? If so, how much change will he get?

Read All About It!

Directions: Write a newspaper article about an event in your neighborhood. Look at a newspaper to find examples of writing for three different purposes: to inform, to entertain, and to persuade. Then, choose a topic and write one type of newspaper article. Make sure to tell about the *who, what, when, where, why,* and *how* of the event.

Instrucciones: *Escribe un artículo de periódico sobre un acontecimiento en tu vecindario. Mira un periódico para encontrar ejemplos de escritura para tres propósitos diferentes: para informar, para entretener y para persuadir. Asegúrate de hablar sobre el* quién, qué, cuándo, dónde, por qué *y* cómo *del acontecimiento.*

My Dog

Directions: Read the passage, then answer the questions.

Instrucciones: *Lee el pasaje, luego contesta las preguntas.*

¹Ricky, the dog who became my best friend, just mysteriously appeared at our house one day. ²My mother said that his arrival was not really mysterious. ³She thought that someone who no longer wanted him dropped him off near our house because that person knew we like dogs. ⁴Because no one else in the family seemed much interested in him, I decided that Ricky was mine and that I would name him. ⁵I named him Ricky because I was watching a singer I admired named Ricky on television when Dog Ricky appeared in our front yard. ⁶Why anyone would not want to keep Ricky I could not understand, for he was a loving dog and a mild-mannered one if **he** did not think he was protecting me from villains. ⁷It is true that I always felt safe when Ricky was around. ⁸With him to protect me, I did not mind being home alone. ⁹Also, I could always count on Ricky to be sympathetic if I thought someone had treated me unfairly or if I had suffered a disappointment of any kind. ¹⁰His understanding eyes helped soothe my bruised heart every time. ¹¹Even when he became old and slow and his vision blurred, Ricky always came to my defense like a fierce tiger. ¹²For my money, he had the best qualities a pet should have: Ricky was loyal and loving.

Fluency Goal: Read 120 words in one minute. The bolded word is the 120th word in the passage.

Meta para la fluidez: Leer 120 palabras en un minuto. La palabra en negrita es la palabra número 120 en el pasaje.

1. Which of these words is used as a transition?

   (A) I

   (B) Why

   (C) Also

   (D) Oh

   (E) None of the above

2. Which is the concluding sentence?

   (A) 1

   (B) 12

   (C) 10

   (D) 9

   (E) None of the above

3. Which is the topic sentence?

   (A) 12

   (B) 6

   (C) 5

   (D) 2

   (E) None of the above

4. Which supporting details did the writer have in her paragraph?

   (A) appearance, name, safe, sympathy

   (B) mystery, name, old, barking

   (C) mother, family, villains, money

   (D) Ricky, singer, safe, eyes, food

   (E) None of the above

Five-Step Plan

Directions: Use the Five-Step Plan to help you solve the word problems.

Instrucciones: *Usa el Plan de cinco pasos para ayudarte a resolver los problemas de planteo.*

Five-Step Plan

1. Read the problem. Make sure you understand the situation.

2. State the problem to be solved.

3. Determine the operation to be used. Do you need to add, subtract, multiply, or divide?

4. Do the operations.

5. Check the final answer to make sure it is reasonable.

Plan de cinco pasos

1. *Lee el problema. Asegúrate que entiendas la situación.*

2. *Expresa el problema que será resuelto.*

3. *Determina la operación que será usada. ¿Necesitas sumar, restar, multiplicar o dividir?*

4. *Haz las operaciones.*

5. *Revisa la respuesta final para asegurarte que sea razonable.*

---

1. Lily had 10 jelly beans evenly distributed into 5 plastic sandwich bags. Her sister Billie had twice the number of jelly beans than in one of Lily's bags. How many jelly beans did Billie have in one bag?

   Billie had _____ jelly beans in one bag.

2. Grady had 10 jelly beans evenly distributed into 2 plastic sandwich bags. His brother Milo had 5 times the number of jelly beans in one of Grady's bags. How many jelly beans did Milo have in one bag?

   Milo had _____ jelly beans in one bag.

The Write Homophones

Directions: The TV announcements below have misused homophones. Rewrite the announcements correcting the homophones.

Instrucciones: *Los anuncios de la tele a continuación han usado homófonos incorrectamente. Reescribe los anuncios corrigiendo los homófonos.*

Tip

Homophones are words that sound alike but are spelled differently and have different meanings.

Los homófonos *son palabras que se oyen igual pero se escriben de manera diferente y tienen significados diferentes.*

---

1. Whether Flash...heavy reigns dew inn an our.

   _____

   _____

2. Next on The Whirled Turns...Elizabeth is never scene again.

   _____

   _____

3. News Extra! A wild hoarse and dear escape from the zoo.

   _____

   _____

4. Watch Mussel Man weakly lift waits on channel too.

   _____

   _____

5. Special Announcement! Ice skating pear wins gold metals!

   _____

   _____

Fun with Factor Pairs

Directions: Write all the factor pairs for each number. Then, choose one factor pair to represent as an array.

Instrucciones: *Escribe todos los pares de factores para cada número. Luego, escoge un par de factores para representarlo como una matriz.*

Tip

A *factor* is a number that divides evenly into another number. *Factor pairs* are two numbers multiplied together to get one number.

Factor pairs of 12 would be 12 and 1, 6 and 2, and 4 and 3.

An array to represent 12 as the factor pair 3 and 4 is:

Un factor *es un número que puede dividirse en partes iguales en otro número.* Pares de factores *son dos números que se multiplican entre sí para obtener un número.*

Pares de factores de 12 serían 12 y 1; 6 y 2; y 4 y 3.

Una matriz para representar 12 con el par de factores 3 y 4 es:

1. 30

3. 16

2. 24

4. 42

Writing by Sense

Directions: Follow the directions below to write sentences using each of the five senses.

Instrucciones: *Sigue las instrucciones a continuación para escribir oraciones usando cada uno de los cinco sentidos.*

Tip

One of the best ways to write descriptively is to use your senses. Think about how something looks, smells, sounds, tastes, and feels, and then write about it, keeping those senses in mind. For example, instead of writing *The puppies are cute*, write *The playful puppies roll over each other and tumble into a ball of fur and pink noses*. This gives an idea of exactly how the puppies look. Sentences that use the senses to describe are much more interesting to read, and they make the images seem real for the reader.

Una de las mejores maneras para escribir descriptivamente es usar tus sentidos. Piensa en cómo algo se ve, huele, suena, sabe y se siente y después escribe sobre ello tomando en cuenta esos sentidos. Por ejemplo, en lugar de escribir "Los cachorros son lindos", escribe "Los cachorros juguetones ruedan unos sobre otros y se enredan en una bola de pelaje y narices rosas". Esto da una idea exacta de cómo se ven los cachorros. Las oraciones que usan los sentidos para describir son mucho más interesantes de leer, y hacen que las imágenes parezcan reales para el lector.

1. Describe how a skyscraper looks. _____

_____

2. Describe how a freshly mowed lawn smells. _____

_____

3. Describe how a yipping dog sounds. _____

_____

4. Describe how a lemon tastes. _____

_____

5. Describe how a kitten feels. _____

_____

Next Stop . . . Decimals!

Directions: Put the towns in order from closest to farthest.

Instrucciones: Escribe las ciudades en orden de la más cercana a la más lejana.

Whistle Stop Train Tours

Train Stops

Newtonville	4.22 miles	North Shore	37.16 miles
Crunch Town	20.07 miles	Dudley Town	27.70 miles
Red River Valley	26.96 miles	St. Barney	35.33 miles
Oakland Hills	10.88 miles	Grovertown	10.19 miles
Raisin City	20.10 miles	Restful Valley	8.18 miles

1. Restful Valley, Raisin City, North Shore

    _____, _____, _____

2. Oakland Hills, Dudley Town, Crunch Town

    _____, _____, _____

3. North Shore, St. Barney, Grovertown

    _____, _____, _____

4. Red River Valley, Dudley Town, North Shore

    _____, _____, _____

5. Restful Valley, Oakland Hills, St. Barney

    _____, _____, _____

Idioms

Directions: Determine the meanings of the idioms below.

Instrucciones: *Determina los significados de los modismos de abajo.*

Idioms are expressions whose meanings are different from the literal meanings.

Los modismos *son expresiones cuyos significados son diferentes de los significados literales.*

1. When Angelica said, "That movie *took my breath away*," she meant _____

   _____

2. "When Dad finally *put his foot down*, my brother started to do better in school," said Boris.
   What Boris meant was _____

   _____

3. Dana stood and said, "I guess I'll *hit the road* now." What Dana meant was _____

   _____

4. When Mario said that he was a bit *under the weather* last weekend, he meant

   _____

5. When Nicholas said that he *slept like a log* last night, he meant _____

   _____

6. "I'll be *in the doghouse* for sure," exclaimed Roberto. Roberto meant _____

   _____

Perpendicular and Parallel Lines

Directions: Draw the polygons described below.

Instrucciones: *Dibuja los polígonos descritos abajo.*

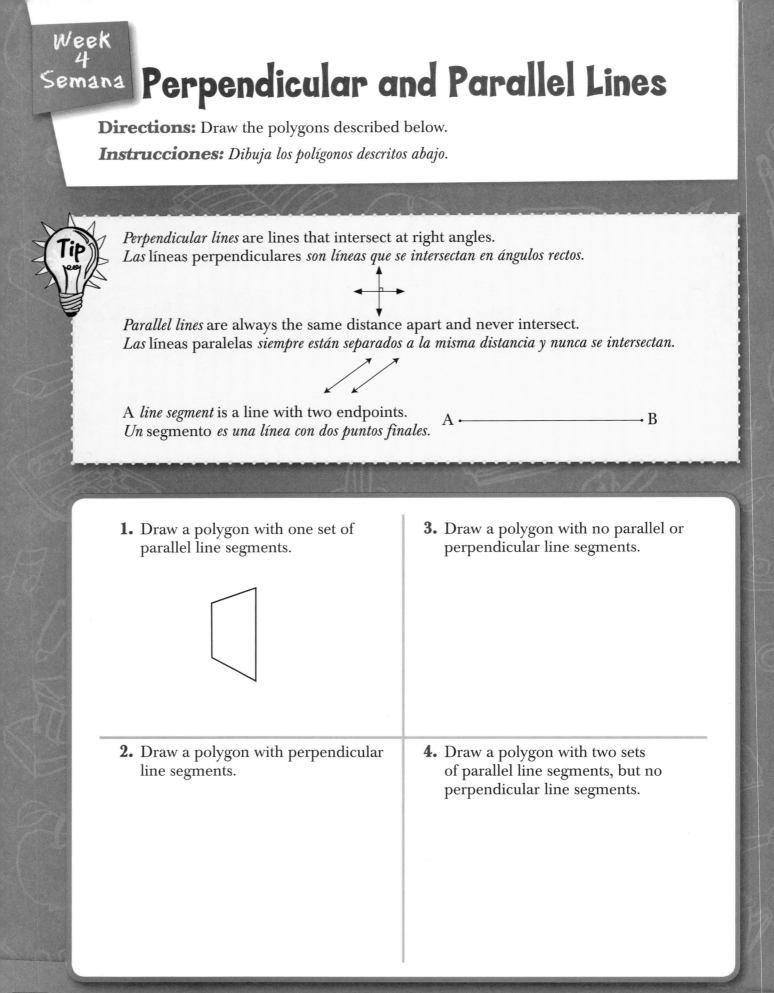

Tip

Perpendicular lines are lines that intersect at right angles.
Las líneas perpendiculares *son líneas que se intersectan en ángulos rectos.*

Parallel lines are always the same distance apart and never intersect.
Las líneas paralelas *siempre están separados a la misma distancia y nunca se intersectan.*

A *line segment* is a line with two endpoints.
Un segmento *es una línea con dos puntos finales.*

A •————————————————• B

---

1. Draw a polygon with one set of parallel line segments.

3. Draw a polygon with no parallel or perpendicular line segments.

2. Draw a polygon with perpendicular line segments.

4. Draw a polygon with two sets of parallel line segments, but no perpendicular line segments.

#13537—Kids Learn! Getting Ready for 5th Grade

© Teacher Created Materials

Getting to the Root of It

Directions: Circle the prefix or suffix in each word. Then, complete the chart with the meaning of each prefix or suffix and the meaning of each word.

Instrucciones: *Encierra con un círculo el prefijo o sufijo de cada palabra. Luego, completa la gráfica con el significado de cada prefijo o sufijo y el significado de cada palabra.*

Word	Prefix/Suffix Meaning	Word Meaning
1. (ir)responsible	not	not responsible
2. misunderstand		
3. meaningful		
4. worthless		
5. immaterial		
6. disengage		
7. unaware		
8. prearrange		
9. semicircle		
10. biweekly		

Prime or Composite?

Directions: Determine whether the numbers are prime or composite. Write *prime* or *composite* on each line. Draw a picture to prove that your answer is correct.

Instrucciones: *Decide si los números son primos o compuestos. Escribe* prime *o* composite *en cada línea.*

 A *composite number* is a number that can be divided evenly and has factors other than itself and 1. A *prime number* is a number that cannot be divided evenly. It can be divided by only 1 and itself.

Un número compuesto *es un número que puede ser dividido en partes iguales y tiene factores aparte de si mismo y 1. Un* número primo *es un número que no puede ser dividido en partes iguales. Puede ser dividido por 1 y por si mismo.*

The number 6 is a composite number. It can be divided evenly.

El número 6 es considerado un número compuesto. Puede ser dividido en partes iguales.

The number 7 is a prime number. It cannot be divided evenly.

El número 7 es un número primo. No puede ser dividido en partes iguales.

1. 8

composite
_____

2. 17

_____

3. 25

_____

4. 31

_____

5. 37

_____

6. 42

_____

You're a Star!

Directions: Imagine that one day you become very famous. Write a story about the success that brings you fame. Give your story a title. In the story, explain how and why you became famous. Also, tell about what other important things you might do in the future.

Instrucciones: *Imagina que un día te haces famoso. Escribe una historia sobre el éxito que te llevo a la fama. Ponle un título a tu historia. En la historia, explica cómo y por qué te hiciste famoso. También cuenta sobre qué otras cosas importantes harás en el futuro.*

YOUR NAME

Getting Online

Directions: Read the passage, then answer the questions.

Instrucciones: *Lee el pasaje, luego contesta las preguntas.*

When you want to play math games, you can go online. But how does that work? How do you get to the math website you want to visit? All computers on the Internet use the same communication language called TCP/IP. When you tell the computer to go to the math website, your computer talks to the math website in TCP/IP. That is how the website knows you want to play a game. When you play a math game, you click or type. Your computer tells the math website what you type or click. It uses TCP/IP to do that. How does your computer know where the website is? Each website has its own address, just as people and businesses do. When you type in the math website's address, the computer finds that place on the World Wide Web.

1. How does a math website know what you type or click?

   (A) You talk to someone at the math website.

   (B) Your computer communicates with the website using TCP/IP.

   (C) The math website reads what you type.

   (D) Your computer tells you what to type or click.

2. Which sentence is a summary sentence?

   (A) the fourth sentence

   (B) the first sentence

   (C) the third sentence

   (D) the second sentence

3. Which syllable is stressed in the word *computer*?

   (A) the first syllable

   (B) the second syllable

   (C) the third syllable

   (D) all of the above

4. Which word has multiple meanings?

   (A) website

   (B) type

   (C) math

   (D) computer

5. *Your computer talks to the math website in TCP/IP* is an example of

   (A) a metaphor

   (B) personification

   (C) hyperbole

   (D) none of the above

Number Sequences

Directions: Determine the missing numbers in each sequence below. Write the rule for each pattern.

Instrucciones: Encuentra el número que falta en cada oración de abajo. Escribe la regla para cada patrón.

1. 0, 3, 6, 9, 12, __15__, __18__, __21__, __24__, __27__

Rule: ___add 3___

2. 1, 6, 11, 16, 21, 26, _____, _____, _____, _____, _____

Rule: _____

3. 7, 14, 28, 56, _____, _____, _____, _____, _____

Rule: _____

4. 800, 400, 200, _____, _____, _____

Rule: _____

5. 97, 90, 83, 76, 69, 62, _____, _____, _____, _____, _____

Rule: _____

6. 1, 7, 13, 19, 25, _____, _____, _____, _____, _____

Rule: _____

7. 0.25, 0.50, 0.75, _____, _____, _____, _____, _____

Rule: _____

8. 3, 30, 300, 3,000, _____, _____, _____

Rule: _____

It's All in the Family

Directions: Circle the letters that need to be capitalized and write the capital letters above each one. If there is a capitalized word that should not be capitalized, draw a line through the letter. Then, rewrite each sentence correctly.

Instrucciones: *Encierra con un círculo las letras que deben escribirse con mayúscula y escribe la letra mayúscula arriba de cada una. Si hay una mayúscula que debería ser minúscula, traza una línea en la letra. Luego, reescribe cada oración correctamente.*

1. (u)ncle Jorge sat on the front Porch.

   Uncle Jorge sat on the front porch.

2. I said, "mom, what I really want to do is stay home!"

3. My Mom and my Dad won't be home until 7 P.M.

4. His grandma made a quilt for his Birthday.

5. My Cousin and my Grandma will be coming with my mom.

6. Our Grandparents have a surprise for Aunt Aimee.

7. I wrote "Dear grandma," at the top of my stationery.

8. I wish my aunt Lydia lived closer to us; She is my favorite Aunt.

9. Then luis stopped and looked behind him.

10. I like to go to grandmother Norton's house in the summer.

Working with Fractions

Directions: Add or subtract the fractions. Draw pictures to help you.

Instrucciones: *Suma o resta las fracciones. Haz dibujos para ayudarte.*

Tip

Adding and subtracting fractions is easy when the denominators (bottom numbers) are the same. Simply add or subtract the numerators (top numbers).

Sumar y restar fracciones es fácil cuando los denominadores (los números de abajo) son iguales. Simplemente suma o resta los numeradores (los números de arriba).

Examples: $\frac{1}{4} + \frac{2}{4} = \frac{3}{4}$

$\frac{5}{7} - \frac{1}{7} = \frac{4}{7}$

---

1. $\frac{3}{4} - \frac{2}{4} =$

2. $\frac{2}{5} + \frac{1}{5} =$

3. $\frac{3}{6} + \frac{2}{6} =$

4. $\frac{2}{9} + \frac{6}{9} =$

5. $\frac{5}{7} - \frac{3}{7} =$

6. $\frac{8}{9} - \frac{4}{9} =$

What Does It Mean?

Directions: Choose the definition that shows how the underlined word is used in each sentence.

Instrucciones: *Escoge la definición que muestra cómo se usa la palabra subrayada en cada oración.*

 **Tip**

Many words have more than one meaning. When reading, you can use *context clues* to determine the meaning of a word in a sentence.

Muchas palabras tienen más de un significado. Cuando leas, puedes usar las pistas de contexto para determinar el significado de una palabra en una oración.

1. Tell me your <u>address</u> so I can find where you live.

   (A) speak or write to

   (B) manner of speech

   (C) place where a person lives

2. Why do you <u>refuse</u> to come to the fair?

   (A) decline to accept

   (B) garbage

   (C) permit to

3. Lost in the <u>desert</u> for hours, the people were hot, hungry, and thirsty.

   (A) dry, sandy wasteland

   (B) abandon

   (C) something deserved

4. The children at <u>play</u> were running and laughing with joy.

   (A) put in motion

   (B) taking part in a game or recreation

   (C) a dramatic work

5. Are there any cookies <u>left</u> for me?

   (A) the westward direction when one is facing north

   (B) remaining

   (C) departed

Mastering Multiplication

Directions: Find each product.

Instrucciones: *Encuentra cada producta.*

1.
$$\begin{array}{r} 369 \\ \times\ \ 5 \\ \hline \textbf{1,845} \end{array}$$

2.
$$\begin{array}{r} 428 \\ \times\ \ 3 \\ \hline \end{array}$$

3.
$$\begin{array}{r} 178 \\ \times\ \ 6 \\ \hline \end{array}$$

4.
$$\begin{array}{r} 933 \\ \times\ \ 8 \\ \hline \end{array}$$

5.
$$\begin{array}{r} 2,365 \\ \times\ \ 4 \\ \hline \end{array}$$

6.
$$\begin{array}{r} 5,302 \\ \times\ \ 7 \\ \hline \end{array}$$

7.
$$\begin{array}{r} 3,964 \\ \times\ \ 4 \\ \hline \end{array}$$

8.
$$\begin{array}{r} 6,203 \\ \times\ \ 5 \\ \hline \end{array}$$

9.
$$\begin{array}{r} 8,427 \\ \times\ \ 9 \\ \hline \end{array}$$

10.
$$\begin{array}{r} 4,004 \\ \times\ \ 6 \\ \hline \end{array}$$

Delete Extra Details

Directions: Read the paragraph below. It has too many details to be a summary. Decide which words or phrases are not important enough to be in a short summary. Cross out the words or phrases that are not important details. To create a summarizing paragraph, rewrite the sentences and words you did not cross out.

Instrucciones: *Lee el párrafo a continuación. Tiene demasiados detalles para ser un resumen. Debes decidir cuáles palabras o frases no son suficientemente importantes para estar en un resumen corto. Tacha las palabras o frases que no son detalles importantes. Para crear un párrafo de resumen, reescribe las oraciones y las palabras que no tachaste.*

Every animal has babies. Sometimes the mother takes care of the baby until it can take care of itself. Baby animals are cute. Sometimes the whole group of animals care for the babies. Baby bears are called cubs. The cubs like to eat honey. Baby animals must eat. Mothers and fathers protect their babies. Some baby animals, like kangaroos, live in pouches. Other baby animals travel on their mothers' backs. Possums and monkeys carry babies on their backs. Baby animals are fun to watch.

Summary

_____

_____

_____

_____

_____

_____

_____

_____

_____

_____

Equivalent Measurements

Directions: Complete the tables with equivalent measurements.

Instrucciones: *Completa las tablas con medidas equivalentes.*

1. **12 in. = 1 ft.**

Inches	Feet
24 in.	2 ft.
48 in.	4 ft.
120 in.	
	5 ft.

5. **100 cm = 1 m**

Centimeters	Meters
400 cm	
660 cm	
	24 m
	8 m

2. **16 oz. = 1 lb.**

Ounces	Pounds
32 oz.	
160 oz.	
96 oz.	
	4 lb.

6. **2,000 lb. = 1 tn.**

Pounds	Tons
8,000 lb.	
14,000 lb.	
	12 tn.
	20 tn.

3. **2 pt. = 1 qt.**

Pints	Quarts
8 pt.	
40 pt.	
	800 qt.
	450 qt.

7. **2 c. = 1 pt.**

Cups	Pints
26 c.	
88 c.	
	40 pt.
	200 pt.

4. **60 min. = 1 hr.**

Minutes	Hours
120 min.	
240 min.	
2,400 min.	
	8 hrs.

8. **60 sec. = 1 min.**

Seconds	Minutes
120 sec.	
1,200 sec.	
	40 min.
	60 min.

Close Reading

Directions: Read the passage, then answer the questions.

Instrucciones: *Lee el pasaje, luego contesta las preguntas.*

The Constitutional Convention was a meeting held in Philadelphia, Pennsylvania. It began in May of 1787 and lasted nearly four months. Each state—except for Rhode Island—sent a representative. Sometimes these men agreed and other times they disagreed. They argued and made changes. Step by step they wrote the United States Constitution. Today it is the supreme law of our land. It created the type of government we have and listed our basic rights.

Clerks used ink and feather quill pens to write the four pages of the Constitution. Then, 39 men signed their names to it. This meant that they agreed with what it said. Some people believe that it is the most important document ever written. No wonder it took so long to write!

1. Who was there?

_____

2. What happened?

_____

3. When?

_____

4. Why?

_____

5. How?

_____

Getting Decimals in Line

Directions: Mark the letter of each value in the correct location on each number line.

Instrucciones: *Marca la letra de cada uno de los valores en el lugar correcto en la línea numérica.*

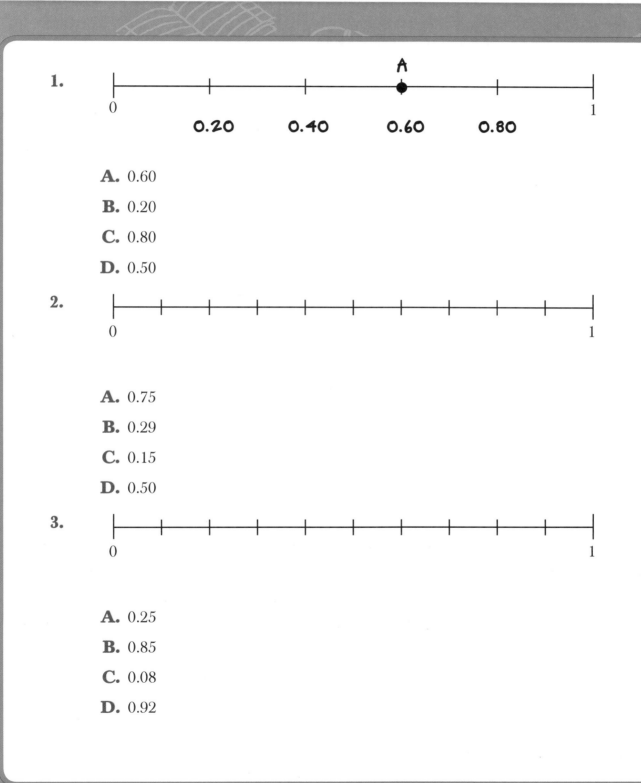

1.

0   0.20   0.40   0.60   0.80   1

A. 0.60

B. 0.20

C. 0.80

D. 0.50

2.

0   1

A. 0.75

B. 0.29

C. 0.15

D. 0.50

3.

0   1

A. 0.25

B. 0.85

C. 0.08

D. 0.92

It's Alive!

Directions: Research one of the three major domains of life (bacteria, archaea, and eukaryota). Use the Internet and/or nonfiction books to learn more about a domain. Write two paragraphs with facts and details about the domain.

Instrucciones: *Investiga uno de los tres principales dominios de seres vivientes (bacteria, arquea y eucaria). Usa la Internet y/o libros de no ficción para aprender más sobre el domio. Escribe dos párrafos con información y detalles sobre el dominio.*

_____

_____

_____

_____

_____

_____

_____

_____

_____

_____

_____

_____

_____

_____

Reading a Recipe

Directions: Read the recipe, then answer the questions.

Instrucciones: *Lee la receta, luego contesta las preguntas.*

Apricot-Banana Shake

Ingredients You Will Need:

1 cup orange juice, chilled

½ cup milk

¼ teaspoon vanilla

1 16-ounce can pitted apricot halves, chilled

1 banana

ground nutmeg

Equipment You Will Need:

measuring cups

can opener

blender

drinking glasses

Directions:

1. Measure the orange juice, milk, and vanilla into the blender. Add the apricots and their juice. Peel the banana. Break the banana into four pieces; add to the blender.

2. With help from an adult, put the lid on the blender and blend the mixture until it is smooth. Pour the mixture into glasses; sprinkle the top with a little nutmeg.

Serve cold and enjoy. Makes 4 servings.

To make your table look special, add a vase of flowers and tie pretty bows around some colorful paper napkins. Use rusts, greens, and browns in the fall. A winter table looks nice with reds and greens and pine cones with ivy or greens from trees. Soft colors and small bunny decorations work well in the spring. Try any flower and color together during the summer. Red, white, and blue decorations make a perfect table for the 4th of July.

1. The recipe could also be called

   (A) "How to Make Your Table Look Special."

   (B) "How to Use a Blender."

   (C) "A Tasty Treat for All Seasons."

   (D) "How to Throw a Summer Party."

2. The last paragraph was written mainly

   (A) to show that the 4th of July is the best time to have a party.

   (B) to show that apricot-banana shakes should only be served on a table.

   (C) to give ideas about how to decorate for the holidays.

   (D) to show how to tie bows around paper napkins.

Relative Sizes of Measurement

Directions: Circle the correct unit of measurement for each problem.

Instrucciones: Encierra con un círculo la unidad de medición para cada problema.

1. Which unit would you use to measure the length of a swimming pool?

   inches   miles   meters

2. Which unit would you use to measure the weight of a blue whale?

   ounces   pounds   tons

3. Which unit would you use to measure the time it takes to watch a movie?

   seconds   hours   days

4. Which unit would you use to measure the amount of liquid in a baby bottle?

   fluid ounces   quarts   gallons

5. Which unit would you use to measure the time it takes to walk to school?

   minutes   days   seconds

6. Which unit would you use to measure the weight of a basketball?

   ounces   pounds   tons

7. Which unit would you use to measure the length of a pencil?

   centimeters   miles   yards

Stop That Sentence!

Directions: Correct each run-on sentence by separating it into two sentences.

Instrucciones: *Corrige cada oración seguida separándola en dos oraciones.*

 **Tip**

A sentence that is too long and runs on to the next thought is called a *run-on sentence*.

Una oración que es muy larga y sigue a la siguiente idea se llama oración seguida.

1. My books are on the table my math book is on top.

   _____

   _____

2. They were closing the store it was time to go home.

   _____

   _____

3. Watch out for the slippery ice you could fall and hurt yourself.

   _____

   _____

4. I got a new blue dress my blue shoes match perfectly.

   _____

   _____

5. My brother made the team will I be able to play baseball someday?

   _____

   _____

More Than a Whole

Directions: Solve each problem. Draw a picture to show your work.

Instrucciones: *Resuelve cada problema. Haz un dibujo para mostrar tu trabajo.*

Tip

A whole number is sometimes involved when adding or subtracting fractions. *Mixed numbers* are numbers that include both a whole number and a fraction, such as $1\frac{3}{5}$. You can add and subtract mixed numbers just like fractions.

Algunas veces un número entero se puede encontrar cuando sumas o restas fracciones. Los números mixtos son números que incluyen tanto un número entero y una fracción, como $1\frac{3}{5}$. Se puede sumar y restar a los números mixtos igual que a las fracciones.

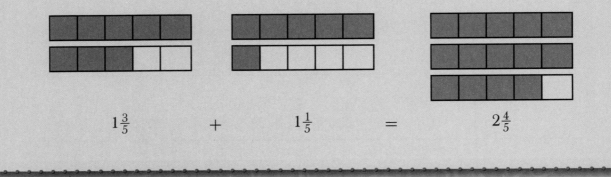

$$1\frac{3}{5} \qquad + \qquad 1\frac{1}{5} \qquad = \qquad 2\frac{4}{5}$$

1. $6\frac{6}{8} - 1\frac{1}{8} =$

2. $12\frac{3}{5} - 6\frac{2}{5} =$

Analyze the Text

Directions: Read the passage, then answer the questions.

Instrucciones: *Lee el pasaje, luego contesta las preguntas.*

Marta and Janis are both eight years old. They have been best friends for two years, even though Marta does not speak much English. Marta is from Mexico. She speaks Spanish very well, a language that Janis does not understand. Marta is teaching Janis to speak Spanish, and Janis is helping Marta to speak better English.

Every afternoon, the girls do their homework together. They munch on their favorite snack, popcorn. Sometimes Janis has to bring her little brother along. He colors in his coloring book while the girls study. Marta loves little Pete, and she wishes she had a baby brother or sister.

After they finish their homework, Marta and Janis go to the city park. Marta takes **her** skates. She is a wonderful skater. Janis brings her scooter. She loves to ride. When Pete comes along, all the children swing and slide. They all enjoy that! It is good to have a best friend!

Fluency Goal: Read 120 words in one minute. The bolded word is the 120th word in the passage.

Meta para la fluidez: Leer 120 palabras en un minuto. La palabra en negrita es la palabra número 120 en el pasaje.

1. How are Marta and Janis alike?

_____

_____

_____

_____

2. How are Marta and Janis different?

_____

_____

_____

_____

Solving by Estimating

Directions: Estimate to solve the problems.

Instrucciones: *Estima para resolver cada problema.*

Example:

Jocelyn played 3 games on a social networking site. She received 321, 489, and 273 points. About how many points all together did Jocelyn earn?

$$300 + 500 + 300 = 1,100$$

---

1. The same number of cats were curled up on each of 5 chairs. A total of 52 cats were curled up on these chairs. About how many cats were on each chair?

2. John's fishing boat caught 2,735 pounds of fish. They put them into boxes of 92 pounds each. About how many boxes did they need?

3. Ann played Math Martians on her computer. She scored 832 in the first game, 505 in the second, and 397 in her last game. About how many points all together did she score?

It's a Matter of Opinion

Directions: Read the opinion piece below. Underline the topic sentence or opinion and circle the supporting rationale. Then, respond to the question.

Instrucciones: *Lee el párrafo de opinión a continuación. Subraya la oración principal o de opinión y encierra con un círculo los detalles que la apoyan. Luego, contesta la pregunta.*

Everybody needs to have a pet. Have you ever noticed that people who do not have pets are grouchier than those who do? If they were greeted whenever they came home by a furry creature thrilled to see them, they would be a lot less grouchy. A pet is affectionate and a good companion. Pets like to snuggle and be with people. Also, pets are always positive. If you give them a special treat, they act as if you've given them the world's largest diamond or the fastest car. They shudder with joy, leap, and prance. If you've had a hard day, they still greet you with enthusiasm. They don't care what you do. You can be a complete failure, and they still treat you as if you are a king or queen. Pets love you unconditionally. If you forget to feed them, they forgive you the moment you remember. Pets are also good safety devices. They can scare away strangers. They can warn you if there is a fire or something wrong inside or outside the house. All they ask in return is a bowl of food, some water, and some TLC (tender, loving care). If everybody had a pet, everybody would go around smiling.

How does the author use reasons and evidence to support the main idea?

_____

_____

_____

_____

_____

_____

_____

_____

_____

_____

More Fraction Fun

Directions: Solve each fraction word problem. *Hint*: Drawing a picture can be helpful.

Instrucciones: *Resuelve cada problema de planteo de fracción.* Pista: *Hacer un dibujo puede ayudarte.*

1. The recipe calls for $\frac{1}{4}$ of a cup of brown sugar and $\frac{1}{4}$ of a cup of white sugar. How much sugar is needed in all?

2. In a glass, Dave mixed $\frac{1}{5}$ of a cup of chocolate milk with $\frac{2}{5}$ of a cup of regular milk. How much liquid is in the glass?

3. Cher used $\frac{1}{3}$ of a cup of red jelly beans and $\frac{1}{3}$ of a cup of green jelly beans. How much did she use in all?

4. To make the dressing, pour $\frac{1}{5}$ of a cup of vinegar and $\frac{3}{5}$ of a cup of oil into a bowl. How much dressing is made?

Evaluating Bias

Directions: Write *F* for fact or *O* for opinion on the line before each statement.

Instrucciones: *Escribe* F *para hecho o* O *para opinión en la línea antes de cada oración.*

> 💡 *Facts* tell only what can be proven. *Biased statements* tell a person's opinion.
>
> *Los* hechos *dicen solo lo que puede ser comprobado.* *Las* declaraciones prejudiciales *dicen opiniones personales.*

_____ **1.** Lions roar loudly.

_____ **2.** Pigs are the laziest of all animals.

_____ **3.** Horses must be brushed often to keep them clean.

_____ **4.** Dogs are better pets than cats.

_____ **5.** The Riverside Zoo was built three years ago.

_____ **6.** More than 400 animals live in the Riverside Zoo.

_____ **7.** The Riverside Zoo is the best zoo in the world.

_____ **8.** The emperor penguin is the most interesting animal to watch.

_____ **9.** Snakes should not be allowed at the zoo because they frighten visitors.

_____ **10.** Polar bears are large, white animals.

How Many Miles?

Directions: Use the diagram to answer the questions.

Instrucciones: *Utiliza el diagrama para contestar las preguntas.*

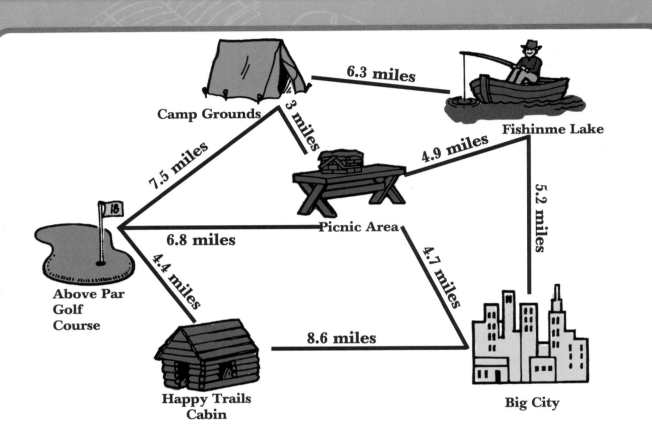

1. How far is it from Happy Trails Cabin to Big City to Fishinme Lake? _____ miles

2. How far is it from Fishinme Lake to Picnic Area to Camp Grounds? _____ miles

3. List the different routes that could be taken to go from Above Par Golf Course to Fishinme Lake and their length.

    A. _____ = _____

    B. _____ = _____

    C. _____ = _____

    D. _____ = _____

4. Which route is the longest? _____

5. Which route is the shortest? _____

6. Are there any routes that are about the same distance? _____

Movie Review

Directions: Using the lines below, write a review of a movie or TV program. Include details about the plot and descriptions of the characters. Give specific details to support your main idea and include how various techniques used by the actors and producers contributed to the message or main idea of the movie.

Instrucciones: *Usando las líneas a continuación, escribe una crítica de una película o un programa de televisión. Incluye detalles de la trama y descripciones de los personajes. Da detalles específicos para apoyar tu idea principal y di como las diferentes técnicas usadas por los actores y productores contribuyeron al mensaje o a la idea principal de la película.*

Preparing Your Child for Assessments

Background for Parents

Many states have recently adopted the Common Core State Standards, a set of national educational standards in language arts and mathematics. These standards provide clear goals for learning in grades K–12 so that all students can gain the skills and knowledge they need to be successful. For more information on the Common Core State Standards, please visit **www.corestandards.org**.

Assessments that are aligned with the Common Core State Standards will replace other state end-of-year tests. These assessments include a variety of types of items. Some items ask students to select the correct option or options from a list. Other items ask students to give a written or numerical response. Students will also complete tasks that gauge their ability to bring together knowledge and skills across many standards.

Preparation Pages

The test preparation items on pages 88–102 provide sample test questions and tasks similar to those that may be found on next-generation assessments. Use the following tips to work through the assessment practice pages with your child:

- Work with your child as he or she completes the practice items so that you can address any questions as they arise.

- Help your child understand how to go about selecting answers or working through tasks.

- Use the Answer Key to check the answers together, and discuss any incorrect responses.

- Keep in mind that for the purposes of this practice, getting the correct answer is not as important as helping your child become comfortable with the test-taking format and process.

#13537—Kids Learn! Getting Ready for 5th Grade

Preparar a su hijo para las evaluaciones

Información general para los padres

Muchos estados recientemente han adoptado los Estándares comunes del estado (Common Core State Standards), un conjunto de estándares educacionales nacionales en artes del lenguaje y matemáticas. Estos estándares proveen metas claras para el aprendizaje en los grados K–12 para que todos los estudiantes puedan lograr las destrezas y el conocimiento que necesitan para ser exitosos. Para más información sobre los Estándares comunes del estado, por favor visite www.corestandards.org.

Las evaluaciones que se ajustan con los Estándares comunes del estado tomarán el lugar de otras pruebas de fin de año del estado. Estas evaluaciones incluyen una variedad de tipos de problemas. Algunos problemas les piden a los estudiantes que escojan la opción correcta u opciones de una lista. Otros problemas les piden a los estudiantes que den una respuesta escrita o numérica. Los estudiantes también completarán tareas que miden su habilidad para unir el conocimiento y las destrezas de muchos estándares.

Páginas de preparación para pruebas

Los problemas de preparación para pruebas en las páginas 88–102 proveen ejemplos de preguntas de pruebas y tareas similares a las que puedan encontrarse en las evaluaciones. Use los siguientes consejos para completar las páginas de preparación para pruebas con su hijo:

- Trabaje junto con su hijo mientras completa los problemas de práctica para que cuando surja cualquier pregunta pueda tratar con ella.

- Ayude a su hijo a entender cómo escoger las respuestas o completar las tareas.

- Use la Hoja de respuestas para juntos revisar las respuestas y analizar cualquier respuesta incorrecta.

- Tenga en cuenta que para los propósitos de esta práctica, obtener la respuesta correcta no es tan importante como ayudar a que su hijo se sienta cómodo con el formato y el proceso de la evaluación.

Language Arts Assessment Practice

Directions: Read the passages, then answer the questions.

A World Under the Water

Do you know how to swim? Some animals know how to swim from the time they are born. They live under the water.

Manatees live underwater. Manatees are gentle animals, but they are big. They can grow up to thirteen feet long. They live in shallow bodies of water. They are migratory animals. They spend winters in Florida's rivers. In the summer, they move northwest. Manatees have been sighted as far north as Massachusetts! They are easy to spot because they are so big and because they are mammals they come to the surface of the water to breathe air. Manatees are always in danger of being hurt or killed by boats.

Blue whales live under the water, too. Blue whales are the largest animals on Earth. An adult blue whale is about the size of a Boeing 838 airplane! They are mammals. Blue whales eat a kind of shrimp called krill. When a blue whale is ready to eat, it swallows a lot of water. Then, it pushes that water out of its mouth with its huge tongue. The krill stay in the whale's mouth. Then, the whale can swallow the krill. Blue whales were hunted for a long time and almost became extinct. People used whale oil for cooking, for lamps, and for other things. They used whalebone because it was light but strong. Finally, laws were made to protect blue whales. Now most countries do not allow blue whale hunting.

Green sea turtles live underwater, too. But they are not mammals. Green sea turtles are reptiles. They live in warm coastal waters. Green sea turtles eat plants that grow underwater. Some green sea turtles come out of the water to warm up on dry land. Female green sea turtles also come out of the water to lay eggs. When the babies are born, they make their way back to the sea. Later, some of those turtles will have babies of their own. Green sea turtles are killed for their meat and their eggs. Green sea turtles can also be hurt by boats and fishing nets.

Manatees, blue whales, and green sea turtles are wonderful sea animals. We need to keep them safe.

1. Explain why the author called manatees "migratory animals." Use details from the text to support your answer.

_____

_____

_____

#13537—Kids Learn! Getting Ready for 5th Grade

Language Arts Assessment Practice (cont.)

2. Which best summarizes the text?

(A) Manatees, blue whales, and green sea turtles are all sea animals. They are all endangered.

(B) Many animals live underwater.

(C) Green sea turtles live in warm coastal areas. They lay eggs on the beach.

(D) There are animals called the manatee, the blue whale, and the green sea turtle.

---

3. Read the sentence and the directions that follow.

> There are many actions people can take to help protect and save manatees, blue whales, and green sea turtles.

Using details from the text, explain the statement above.

_____

_____

_____

_____

Language Arts Assessment Practice *(cont.)*

4. The author most likely wrote the text to

    (A) tell about animals that live underwater.

    (B) tell how to catch a manatee.

    (C) explain that special sea animals are endangered.

    (D) tell about ocean plant life.

---

5. Underline the sentences from the text below that best support your answer above.

> Blue whales live under the water, too. Blue whales are the largest animals on Earth. An adult blue whale is about the size of a Boeing 838 airplane! They are mammals. Blue whales eat a kind of shrimp called krill. When a blue whale is ready to eat, it swallows a lot of water. Then, it pushes that water out of its mouth with its huge tongue. The krill stay in the whale's mouth. Then, the whale can swallow the krill. Blue whales were hunted for a long time and almost became extinct. People used whale oil for cooking, for lamps, and for other things. They used whalebone because it was light but strong. Finally, laws were made to protect blue whales. Now, most countries do not allow blue whale hunting.

90

#13537—Kids Learn! Getting Ready for 5th Grade

© *Teacher Created Materials*

Language Arts Assessment Practice (cont.)

The Crow and the Pitcher

Once there was a crow who was very thirsty. As he flew over the pastoral countryside, he saw an old pitcher sitting near a house.

"Maybe there's water in that pitcher!" he thought as he flew down.

The crow landed near the black and gold vessel and looked inside. There was water in it–at the bottom. He stuck his beak inside, but the pitcher was too tall. He couldn't reach the water. The sun rose high in the sky, and the crow grew even more parched.

"If I don't get some water soon, I'll die!" he croaked.

He had to get that water, but what could he do? If he turned the pitcher over, the water would run out onto the ground. He looked about, trying to think of a way to get the water. Then he saw a small pebble lying on the ground.

Suddenly, he had an idea. He picked the pebble up in his beak and dropped it in the pitcher. It made a soft plunking noise as it hit the water. He realized how nicely that would work. Quickly, he gathered more stones. One by one, he dropped them into the pitcher. Slowly, the level of the water began to rise. When it got high enough, the crow stuck his beak in the pitcher and had a long, cool drink.

6. What caused the water in the pitcher to rise?

_____

_____

_____

Language Arts Assessment Practice *(cont.)*

7. What was the crow's problem?

     (A) He was very hungry.

     (B) He was lost.

     (C) He could not fly.

     (D) He was thirsty.

---

8. Support your answer above with details from the passage.

_____

_____

_____

_____

---

9. Read the passage below and the directions that follow.

The crow landed near the black and gold <u>vessel</u> and looked inside. There was water in it—at the bottom. He stuck his beak inside, but the pitcher was too tall. He couldn't reach the water. The sun rose high in the sky, and the crow grew even more parched.

What does <u>vessel</u> mean as used in the sentence?

_____

_____

#13537—Kids Learn! Getting Ready for 5th Grade

Language Arts Assessment Practice (cont.)

10. Read the sentence below and the directions that follow.

> The crow is clever.

Use details from the passage on page 91 to support the sentence.

_____

_____

_____

_____

11. A student is writing an opinion letter to her teacher about dogs. Read the passage. Then, answer the question that follows.

> If you are looking for a family dog, the Labrador Retriever might be the dog for you. Labradors (also called Labs) are originally from Newfoundland. They are popular all over the world. In fact, Labs are the most popular breed of dog in the United States! They were first bred to work with fishermen. Soon, they became skilled hunting dogs. Now, Labs are also gentle family pets. They like to be active. They also enjoy being with families. They are smart and learn fast.

Which sentence is the best closing statement for the passage?

(A) Labs are also popular in Newfoundland.

(B) If you choose a Lab for a pet it is sure to be friendly and loving.

(C) Even if you don't hunt, Labs are a great dog.

(D) Labs come in three different colors: black, chocolate, and yellow.

Language Arts Assessment Practice *(cont.)*

12. A student wrote a sentence that contains errors in punctuation. Underline the word or words that should be followed by a comma.

> You can choose from a variety of careers like teacher doctor lawyer bus driver or banker.

---

13. Miguel is writing an informal report on the rainforest. Read the report and the directions that follow.

> (1) The Amazon Rainforest is special. It is home to one-half of the world's species. (2) The Amazon River flows through the rainforest. (3) Eventually, it ends in the Atlantic Ocean. (4) Many animals live in the river. (5) Other animals live in the forest. (6) The Amazon is a tropical rainforest. (7) That means there are high temperatures and a lot of rain. (8) It provides water, trees, and oxygen for us. (9) It is home to many animals. (10) We need to protect this special place. (11) If we do not, we could lose it.

Miguel wants to revise the report by adding more information after sentence 7. Which sentence best supports the topic of the report?

- **(A)** The rainforest gets over fifty-nine inches of rain per year!

- **(B)** Unlike the desert, plants and animals depend on the water.

- **(C)** Brazil is home to many acres of rainforest.

- **(D)** The rainforest provides plants, oxygen, and water to the world.

#13537—Kids Learn! Getting Ready for 5th Grade

© *Teacher Created Materials*

Language Arts Assessment Practice (cont.)

14. Read the passage below and the directions that follow.

Have you ever heard of the Pentagon? It is an important building in Virginia. <u>The prefix</u> <u>*penta-* means "five" so how many sides does the Pentagon have</u>? If you guessed five, you're right!

Choose the sentence that is punctuated correctly.

Ⓐ The prefix *penta-* means "five" so, how many sides does the Pentagon have?

Ⓑ The prefix *penta-* means "five," so how many sides does the Pentagon have!

Ⓒ The prefix *penta-* means "five," so how many sides does the Pentagon have?

Ⓓ The prefix *penta-* means five, so how many sides does the Pentagon have.

15. Which best describes the tone of the passage above?

Ⓐ absurd

Ⓑ silly

Ⓒ depressing

Ⓓ engaging

Mathematics Assessment Practice

Directions: Solve the problems.

1.

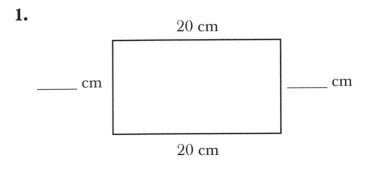

20 cm

_____ cm

_____ cm

20 cm

The area of this field is 360 cm². Write the distance of the missing sides on the lines above.

What is the perimeter, in centimeters, of the field?

---

2. Is the number 18 prime?   Yes   No

 2a. Explain your answer.

_____

_____

_____

#13537—Kids Learn! Getting Ready for 5th Grade   © *Teacher Created Materials*

Mathematics Assessment Practice *(cont.)*

3. Choose the correct numbers from the box to complete the chart.

1 2 3 4 5 6 7 8 9 10 11

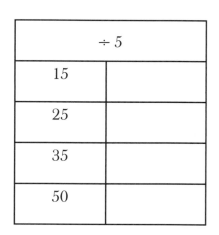

	÷ 5
15	
25	
35	
50	

---

4. Lucy and Max worked together to make 84 key chains for the school craft fair. They are working on a display to show their key chains. Mark the possible arrangements for the display. Write *yes* or *no* on each line.

4a. 2 rows of 42 _____

4b. 5 rows of 15 _____

4c. 3 rows of 26 _____

4d. 4 rows of 21 _____

4e. 12 rows of 7 _____

4f. 16 rows of 8 _____

4g. 14 rows of 6 _____

5. Raymond has a piece of string that is $\frac{8}{9}$ inches long. He cuts the string so that one piece is $\frac{3}{9}$ inches long. How long is the other piece?

(A) $\frac{11}{9}$ inch

(B) $\frac{4}{9}$ inch

(C) $\frac{5}{9}$ inch

(D) $\frac{3}{9}$ inch

6. While three kids are playing a game, the board gets knocked over. Mark the spaces on the game board where each piece was before being knocked over.

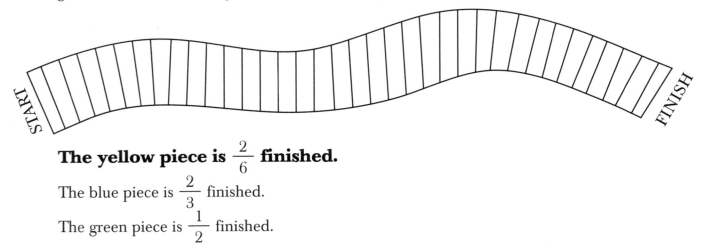

The yellow piece is $\frac{2}{6}$ finished.

The blue piece is $\frac{2}{3}$ finished.

The green piece is $\frac{1}{2}$ finished.

6a. Who is closest to the finish? Explain how you know.

_____

_____

_____

Mathematics Assessment Practice *(cont.)*

7. Marnie saves $5.00 each week for a new $36.00 sweater. She has saved for 3 weeks.

    7a. How much has she saved? _____

    7b. How much more does she need? _____

    7c. How many more weeks will it take her to purchase the sweater? _____

    7d. If she starts saving $8.00 a week how long will it take her? _____

---

8. Label the parts of this circle using the Number Bank.

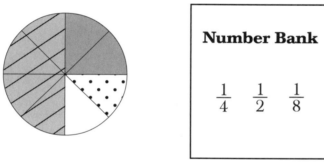

Number Bank

$\frac{1}{4}$ $\frac{1}{2}$ $\frac{1}{8}$

8a. Explain why you labeled the largest part of the circle the way you did.

_____

_____

_____

_____

8b. What fraction of the circle remains unlabeled?

_____

Mathematics Assessment Practice *(cont.)*

9. Use the numbers in the box to complete the addition problem shown.

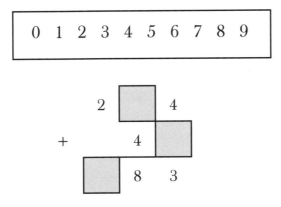

0 1 2 3 4 5 6 7 8 9

---

10. Use the numbers in the box once to complete the comparisons below.

88 97 225 975 59

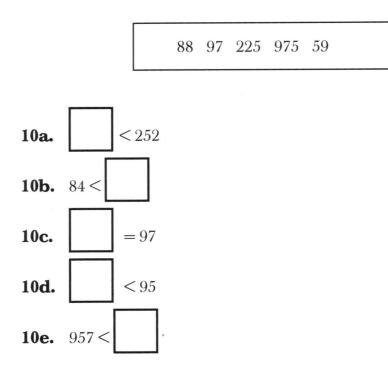

10a. ☐ < 252

10b. 84 < ☐

10c. ☐ = 97

10d. ☐ < 95

10e. 957 < ☐

#13537—Kids Learn! Getting Ready for 5th Grade

Mathematics Assessment Practice (cont.)

11. Which of the following expressions have a sum equal to $\frac{81}{100}$?

- **A** $\frac{8}{10} + \frac{1}{100}$

- **B** $\frac{80}{10} + \frac{1}{100}$

- **C** $\frac{7}{10} + \frac{11}{100}$

- **D** $\frac{31}{100} + \frac{50}{100}$

- **E** $\frac{6}{10} + \frac{31}{100}$

---

12. Write each of the expressions in the appropriate location on the chart.

$\frac{1}{3} \times 2$

$\frac{3}{4} \times 3$

$\frac{2}{4} \times 3$

$\frac{1}{6} \times 5$

$\frac{3}{9} \times 6$

$\frac{5}{7} \times 2$

$\frac{2}{8} \times 2$

Less than 1	Greater than 1

---

13. Round the number 3,495 to the thousands place. _____

13a. Explain why you rounded to the number in your answer.

_____

_____

_____

Mathematics Assessment Practice (cont.)

14. Raul and Tommy are playing a dice game. They are using each digit they roll to build numbers. Raul rolls the five dice below.

14a. Tommy says the largest odd number Raul can build is 63,425. Is Tommy correct?

_____

14b. Why or why not?

_____

_____

_____

15. Mark the shapes that have one or more lines of symmetry.

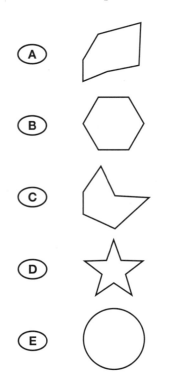

Ⓐ

Ⓑ

Ⓒ

Ⓓ

Ⓔ

#13537—Kids Learn! Getting Ready for 5th Grade   © *Teacher Created Materials*

Great Work!

(Name)

**has completed
Kids Learn! Getting Ready for 5th Grade**

(Date)

Answer Key

Page 20
1. B
2. B
3. A
4. C

Page 21
1. Drawing should show 3 groups of 9; 27 is the same as 3 sets of 9; 27 is the same as 3 times 9.
2. Drawing should show 5 groups of 6; 30 is the same as 5 sets of 6; 30 is the same as 5 times 6.

Page 22
1. explicit
2. implicit
3. implicit
4. explicit
5. implicit

Page 23
1. a. 50
   b. 4th grade
2. a. 98 km
   b. no
3. a. $284.95
   b. yes
4. a. 7
   b. 13

Page 24
Answers will vary.

Page 25
Pictures will vary.

1. $6 \times \dfrac{1}{4}$ six fourths;
2. $8 \times \dfrac{1}{5}$ eight fifths;
3. $5 \times \dfrac{1}{3}$ five thirds;

Page 26
Answers will vary. Possible definitions:
1. to persuade
2. at night
3. exhausted
4. large

Page 27
1. +
2. −, +, +
3. +, −
4. −, +
5. +, +, +, −
6. +, +
7. −, +, +, +, +
8. −, +, −
9. −, +
10. +, −, − or +, +, + or − + −

Page 28
Answers will vary.

Page 29
Across:
1. fourteen
3. nineteen
7. seventeen
9. sixteen
Down:
1. fifteen
2. twenty
4. eighteen
5. eleven
6. twelve
8. thirteen

Page 30
Answers will vary.

Page 31
1. A
2. B

Page 32
1. 15 ft.²
2. 2,880 in.²
3. 2,322 cm.²
4. 1,250 m.²
5. 108 ft.²

Page 33
Answers will vary.

Page 34
1.

	x		x				
x	x	x	x	x			x
x	x	x	x	x	x	x	x
1 in.	$1\frac{1}{4}$ in.	$1\frac{3}{4}$ in.	2 in.	$2\frac{1}{2}$ in.	$2\frac{3}{4}$ in.	$3\frac{1}{4}$ in.	$3\frac{1}{2}$ in.

2. $1\frac{3}{4}$ inches and $2\frac{1}{2}$ inches
3. $3\frac{1}{2}$ inches
4. 1 inch
5. $2\frac{1}{2}$ inches
6. Answers will vary.

Page 35
Answers will vary but should reflect these ideas:
1. Lola
2. loves to watch parrots
3. They are her favorite animals at the zoo.
4. Lola loves to watch parrots because they are her favorite animals at the zoo.

Page 36
1. 2,862
2. 900
3. 2,592
4. 1,127
5. 1,242
6. 4,028
7. 1,943
8. 3,510

Page 37
Answers will vary.

Page 38
1. 30°; acute angle
2. 90°; right angle
3. 170°; obtuse angle
4. 60°; acute angle

Answer Key (cont.)

Page 39
1. Yes, we go to the library on Tuesday.
2. Mrs. Smith is your teacher.
3. The students in Mr. Garcia's class were reading <u>Charlotte's Web.</u>
4. What a wonderful day it is!
5. Jordan, come play with us in Griffith Park.
6. Watch out, Michelle!
7. Maria, what is your favorite kind of math problem?
8. I will paint John's room today.

Page 40
1. $\frac{3}{5}$
2. $\frac{5}{6}$
3. $\frac{6}{8}$ or $\frac{3}{4}$
4. $\frac{10}{12}$ or $\frac{5}{6}$
5. $\frac{9}{14}$
6. $\frac{10}{7}$ or $1\frac{3}{7}$

Page 41
Answers will vary.

Page 42
Answers will vary but should reflect these ideas.
1. Tia didn't do anything when the bully bullied her. She was too ashamed.
2. She didn't bully anyone else because she didn't want to be a bully.
3. Tia told the bully to stop picking on her friend.
4. The story could have ended differently if Tia had been a bully back to one of the girls.

Page 43
1. 602 R3
2. 1,217 R2
3. 1,502 R3
4. 809 R4
5. 979
6. 1,210 R5
7. 502
8. 2,024
9. 1,158 R3

Page 44
Time-order words added will vary. The sequence of the sentences should be as follows:
I woke up one morning…
I got out of bed…
What a shock I got when…
I ran to my mother…
She said, "It appears those seeds…"
Then she looked…
I am feeling better now…

Page 45
1. 6,000; 6,400; 6,410
2. 8,000; 7,500; 7,520
3. 3,000; 3,100; 3,100
4. Answers will vary, but may include estimating costs or measurements.

Page 46
Answers will vary. Possible answers:
1. joy, sadness
2. enrage, delight
3. accomplished, amateur
4. ardent, cold

Page 47
1. <
2. <
3. =
4. >
5. <
6. >
7. <
8. >
9. <
10. Answers will vary.

Page 48
Crossed out sentences:
I got a good grade on my homework assignment, though.
Last week at school I had hall duty.
Our home fireplace uses gas.
I can't remember whether I put plenty of food in my fish tank at home.
My mother says that the fish at our local market do not always seem fresh to her.

Page 49
1. 5; 5,000
2. 6; 600
3. 20; 20
4. 270; 2,700
5. 35.6; 35,600
6. 8,700; 8,700
7. 7.1; 7,100
8. 91,000; 91,000

Page 50
1. that
2. who
3. whose
4. which
5. whom
6. which

Page 51
1. 47 stamps
2. 11 strawberries
3. Yes; 3 slices
4. Yes; $0.25

Page 52
Answers will vary.

Page 53
1. C
2. B
3. E
4. A

Page 54
1. 4
2. 25

#13537—Kids Learn! Getting Ready for 5th Grade

Answer Key (cont.)

Page 55
1. Weather Flash...heavy rains due in an hour.
2. Next on *The World Turns...* Elizabeth is never seen again.
3. News Extra! A wild horse and deer escape from the zoo.
4. Watch Muscle Man weekly lift weights on channel two.
5. Special Announcement! Ice skating pair wins gold medals.

Page 56
1. 30: 30 and 1; 10 and 3; 6 and 5; 15 and 2; Arrays will vary.
2. 24: 24 and 1; 12 and 2; 6 and 4; 8 and 3; Arrays will vary.
3. 16: 16 and 1; 8 and 2; 4 and 4; Arrays will vary.
4. 42: 42 and 1; 21 and 2; 14 and 3; 7 and 6; Arrays will vary.

Page 57
Answers will vary.

Page 58
1. Restful Valley, Raisin City, North Shore
2. Oakland Hills, Crunch Town, Dudley Town
3. Grovertown, St. Barney, North Shore
4. Red River Valley, Dudley Town, North Shore
5. Restful Valley, Oakland Hills, St. Barney

Page 59
Answers will vary. Possible answers:
1. It was amazing.
2. His father got serious and set rules or limits.
3. She was ready to leave.
4. He had not felt well.
5. He slept soundly.
6. He was going to be in trouble.

Page 60
Answers will vary. Possible answers:

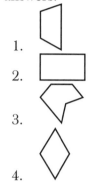

1.
2.
3.
4.

Page 61
1. ir; not; not responsible
2. mis; wrong; wrong understanding
3. ful; full of; full of meaning
4. less; without; without worth
5. im; not; not material
6. dis; not; not engaged
7. un; not; not aware
8. pre; before; arrange before
9. semi; half; half circle
10. bi; two; every two weeks

Page 62
1. composite
2. prime
3. composite
4. prime
5. prime
6. composite

Page 63
Answers will vary.

Page 64
1. B
2. A
3. B
4. B
5. B

Page 65
1. 15, 18, 21, 24, 27; add 3
2. 31, 36, 41, 46, 51; add 5
3. 112, 224, 448, 896, 1792; multiply by 2
4. 100, 50, 25; divide by 2
5. 55, 48, 41, 34, 27; subtract 7
6. 31, 37, 43, 49, 55; add 6
7. 1.00, 1.25, 1.50, 1.75, 2.00; add 0.25
8. 30,000; 300,000; 3,000,000; multiply by 10

Page 66
1. Uncle Jorge sat on the front porch.
2. I said, "Mom, what I really want to do is to stay home!"
3. My mom and my dad won't be home until 7 p.m.
4. His grandma made a quilt for his birthday.
5. My cousin and my grandma will be coming with my mom.
6. Our grandparents have a surprise for Aunt Aimee.
7. I wrote "Dear Grandma," at the top of my stationery.
8. I wish my aunt Lydia lived closer to us; she is my favorite aunt.
9. Then Luis stopped and looked behind him.
10. I like to go to Grandmother Norton's house in the summer.

Answer Key *(cont.)*

Page 67

1. $\dfrac{1}{4}$

2. $\dfrac{3}{5}$

3. $\dfrac{5}{6}$

4. $\dfrac{8}{9}$

5. $\dfrac{2}{7}$

6. $\dfrac{4}{9}$

Page 68

1. C
2. A
3. A
4. B
5. B

Page 69

1. 1,845
2. 1,284
3. 1,068
4. 7,464
5. 9,460
6. 37,114
7. 15,856
8. 31,015
9. 75,843
10. 24,024

Page 70

Answers will vary.
Suggested details to leave out:
Baby animals are cute.
Baby bears are called cubs.
The cubs like to eat honey.
Baby animals must eat.
Baby animals are fun to watch.

Page 71

1. 2 ft., 4 ft., 10 ft, 60 in.
2. 2 lb., 10 lb., 6 lb., 64 oz.
3. 4 qt., 20 qt., 1,600 pt., 900 pt.
4. 2 hrs., 4 hrs., 40 hrs., 480 min.
5. 4 m, 6.6 m, 2,400 cm, 800 cm
6. 4 tn., 7 tn., 24,000 lb., 40,000 lb.
7. 13 pt., 44 pt., 80 c., 400 c.
8. 2 min., 20 min., 2,400 sec., 3,600 sec.

Page 72

1. representatives from each state except Rhode Island
2. met at Constitutional Convention
3. May to August, 1787
4. to write the U.S. Constitution
5. by debating and voting

Page 73

1.

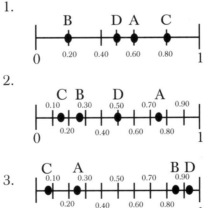

2.

3.

Page 74

Answers will vary.

Page 75

1. C
2. C

Page 76

1. meters
2. tons
3. hours
4. fluid ounces
5. minutes
6. pounds
7. centimeters

Page 77

1. My books are on the table. My math book is on top.
2. They were closing the store. It was time to go home.
3. Watch out for the slippery ice. You could fall and hurt yourself.
4. I got a new blue dress. My blue shoes match perfectly.
5. My brother made the team. Will I be able to play baseball someday?

Page 78

1. $5\dfrac{5}{8}$

2. $6\dfrac{1}{5}$

Page 79

Answers will vary. Possible answers:

1. eight years old, best friends, teaching each other their primary language, do homework together, popcorn is favorite snack, love Pete, enjoy the park, play with Pete in the park
2. Marta doesn't speak English well and Janis doesn't speak Spanish well, Janis has a little brother and Marta has no siblings, Marta is a good skater, Janis has a scooter

108

#13537—Kids Learn! Getting Ready for 5th Grade

© *Teacher Created Materials*

Answer Key (cont.)

Page 80
1. 10 cats
2. 30 boxes
3. 1,700 points

Page 81
Answers will vary.
1. The author supports the main idea with reasons and evidence that will convince the reader to believe.

Page 82
1. $\frac{2}{4}$ or $\frac{1}{2}$ of a cup of sugar
2. $\frac{3}{5}$ of a cup of liquid
3. $\frac{2}{3}$ of a cup in all
4. $\frac{4}{5}$ of a cup of dressing

Page 83
1. F
2. O
3. F
4. O
5. F
6. F
7. O
8. O
9. O
10. F

Page 84
1. 13.8 miles
2. 7.9 miles
3. Sample answers:
a. Golf Course to Picnic Area to Lake = 11.7 miles
b. Golf Course to Cabin to Big City to Lake = 18.2 miles
c. Golf Course to Camp to Lake = 13.8 miles
d. Golf Course to Cabin to Big City to Picnic Area to Lake = 22.6 miles
4. Answers will vary depending on routes chosen.
5. Answers will vary depending on routes chosen.
6. Answers will vary depending on routes chosen.

Page 85
Answers will vary.

Language Arts Assessment Practice
1. Answers will vary. Possible answer: Migratory means they move around from place to place. Manatees live in Florida for the winter and move northwest in the summer.
2. A
3. Answers will vary. Possible answer: People can help endangered sea animals like the manatee, blue whale, and green sea turtle by being careful when they boat so they do not harm the animals and their habitats. People can pass laws protecting endangered animals like many countries have for the blue whale. Lastly, fishermen should use nets designed to capture only the fish they intend to catch and not larger animals like the green sea turtle.
4. C
5. The following sentences should be underlined: <u>Blue whales were hunted for a long time and almost became extinct.</u> and <u>Finally, laws were made to protect blue whales. Now, most countries do not allow blue whale hunting.</u>
6. Answers will vary. Possible answer: The water in the pitcher rose because the pebbles were dropped in and took up space.
7. D
8. Answers will vary. Possible answer: The passage says the crow is thirsty and all of his actions throughout the story are to get water from the pitcher.

9. Answers will vary. Possible answer: In the story, vessel means pitcher or container that holds water.
10. Answers will vary. Possible answer: The crow is clever because he figures out how to drop rocks into the pitcher to make the water rise enough to drink it.
11. B
12. You can choose from a variety of <u>careers</u>, like <u>teacher</u> <u>doctor</u> <u>lawyer</u> bus <u>driver</u> and banker.
13. A
14. C
15. D

Mathematics Assessment Practice
1. The sides of the rectangle are 18, 20, 18, 20; The perimeter is 76 cm.
2. No
2a. Answers will vary. Possible answer: 18 isn't prime because it has factors of 1, 2, 3, 6, 9, and 18.
3.

÷ 5	
15	3
25	5
35	7
50	10

4a. yes
4b. no
4c. no
4d. yes
4e. yes
4f. no
4g. yes
5. C
6. Yellow should be on space 12
Blue should be on space 24
Green should be on space 18

Answer Key (cont.)

6a. Answers will vary. Possible answer: Blue is closest to the finish because

$$\frac{2}{3} > \frac{1}{2} > \frac{2}{6} .$$

7a. $15.00
7b. $21.00
7c. 5 weeks
7d. 3 weeks

8.

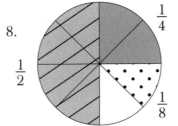

$\frac{1}{4}$

$\frac{1}{2}$

$\frac{1}{8}$

8a. Answers will vary. Possible answer: I labeled the largest part $\frac{1}{2}$ because $\frac{1}{2} = \frac{4}{8}$.

8b. $\frac{1}{8}$ of the circle remains unlabeled.

9. $234 + 49 = 283$

10. Accept any correct answer. Possible answers include:

10a. $225 < 252$
10b. $84 < 88$
10c. $97 = 97$
10d. $59 < 95$
10e. $957 < 975$

11. A, C, and D

12.

Less than 1	Greater than 1
$\frac{2}{8} \times 2$	$\frac{5}{7} \times 2$
$\frac{1}{6} \times 5$	$\frac{3}{9} \times 6$
$\frac{1}{3} \times 2$	$\frac{2}{4} \times 3$
	$\frac{3}{4} \times 3$

13. 3,000
13a. Answers will vary. Possible answer: I rounded to 3,000 because it is closer to 3,495 than 4,000.
14a. No
14b. Answers will vary. Possible answer is: $63,425 < 65,423$.
15. Answers B, D, and E should be marked.

Kids Learn! Parent Survey

Dear Parent,

The activities in this *Kids Learn!* book have helped your child review grade-level skills from the recent school year and get ready for the year ahead. Your feedback on this learning resource is very valuable. Please complete the survey below and return it as directed by your child's teacher or school administrator. Thank you in advance for your input and your time.

Please circle the term that best describes how you feel about this *Kids Learn!* book.

1. The **Introduction** (pages 4–18) gave me good ideas for things to do with my child and offered helpful resources for extended learning.

   Strongly Agree   Agree   Disagree   Strongly Disagree

2. The **Weekly Activities for Students** (pages 19–85) were easy to understand and helped me guide my child to complete the activity sheets. The activities were at an appropriate level of difficulty for my child.

   Strongly Agree   Agree   Disagree   Strongly Disagree

3. The **Assessment Practice** (pages 86–102), which shows the types of questions that will be on Common Core State Standards annual assessments, gave me and my child a better understanding of the standardized tests and how to prepare for them.

   Strongly Agree   Agree   Disagree   Strongly Disagree

4. The sections of *Kids Learn!* that were particularly helpful or useful for me and my child were: *(Please check all that apply.)*

   ☐ Top 10 Things Your Fifth Grader Will Need to Know   ☐ Websites and Apps for Parents and Kids

   ☐ Things to Do at Home   ☐ Weekly Activities for Students

   ☐ Things to Do in the Community   ☐ Preparing Your Child for Assessments

   ☐ Suggested Vacation Reading and Log

Please provide any additional comments or suggestions about this *Kids Learn!* book.

_____

_____

_____

Kids Learn! Encuesta para los padres

Querido padre de familia:

Las actividades en este libro *Kids Learn!* han ayudado a su hijo a repasar las destrezas de nivel de grado del reciente año escolar y a prepararse para el año siguiente. Sus comentarios sobre este recurso educativo son muy valiosos. Por favor, complete la encuesta a continuación y regrésela como lo indica el maestro o administrador escolar de su hijo. Le agradecemos de antemano por su participación y por su tiempo.

Por favor encierre con un círculo el término que mejor describe su opinión sobre este libro *Kids Learn!*

1. La **Introducción** (páginas 4–18) me dio buenas ideas de cosas que hacer con mi hijo y me ofrecieron recursos útiles para ampliar el aprendizaje.

   Totalmente de acuerdo   De acuerdo   En desacuerdo   Totalmente en desacuerdo

2. Las **Actividades semanales para los estudiantes** (páginas 19–85) eran fáciles de entender y me ayudaron a guiar a mi hijo a completar las hojas de ejercicios. Las actividades eran de un nivel de dificultad adecuado para mi hijo.

   Totalmente de acuerdo   De acuerdo   En desacuerdo   Totalmente en desacuerdo

3. La **Práctica para la evaluación** (páginas 86–102), muestra los tipos de preguntas que vendrán en las evaluaciones anuales de Estándares comunes del estado (*Common Core State Standards*), nos dio a mí y a mi hijo un mejor entendimiento de los exámenes estandarizados y de cómo prepararse.

   Totalmente de acuerdo   De acuerdo   En desacuerdo   Totalmente en desacuerdo

4. Las secciones de *Kids Learn!* que fueron particularmente útiles o nos ayudaron a mí y a mi hijo fueron: *(Por favor marque todas las que sean pertinentes)*.

   ☐ Las 10 cosas que su hijo de quinto grado debe saber

   ☐ Cosas para hacer en casa

   ☐ Cosas para hacer en la comunidad

   ☐ Registro de lectura y la lectura sugerida para las vacaciones

   ☐ Páginas web y aplicaciones para padres y niños

   ☐ Actividades semanales para estudiantes

   ☐ Preparar a su hijo para las evaluaciones

Por favor proporcione cualquier comentario o sugerencia adicional sobre este libro *Kids Learn!*

_____